Bum Jobs

SIMON MAYLE

BUM JOBS

*The Life and Times
of a Man a Long Way
from the Career Path*

SINCLAIR-STEVENSON

First published in Great Britain 1993
by Sinclair-Stevenson
an imprint of Reed Consumer Books Ltd
Michelin House, 81 Fulham Road, London SW3 6RB
and Auckland, Melbourne, Singapore and Toronto

A CIP catalogue record for this book
is available at the British Library

ISBN 1 85619 2164

Typeset by Centracet, Cambridge
Printed in Great Britain
by Clays Ltd, St Ives Plc

To Abner.

One

A little man I know never draws a picture of a house with a path. The boy is five years old and if you were to ask him why he never puts a path in his picture, he'd always say, 'Why? I don't know where it's going.' I'd have to say this is one of the smartest little men I've met in a long time.

I came to New York City from California, earlier from England, where I was born. I arrived with a bag, a skateboard, and no particular purpose. That was about twelve years ago.

My first home in the city was up in Spanish Harlem at 105th Street. It was with a girl who advertised in the back of the *Village Voice*. The room was in a walk-up. The rent for the room was just over two hundred dollars a month. The girl wanted to be an artist. The first day we met, she asked me what I wanted to be in life. I didn't know, I couldn't answer her, so I smiled and I shrugged. But that was all right. She gave me the room, I gave her the money, and we became friends, for a while.

I got night-work at O'Neal's restaurant on 6th Avenue at 57th as a busboy, and, not long after, a day job working for a Canadian photographer down on 23rd Street. The photographer was a piece of work. His photographs were schlock, like all catalogue crap that appears in the mail-box unwanted. But he thought he was the next Irving Penn. He often told me how his talent would elevate him to the position of respect of a Mr Penn, or a Mr Scavullo –

those were his favourite big cameras – and I'd listen, nod and try not to laugh my head off.

I worked cleaning his studio, propping his lights, lifting his fill cards, making his coffee, carrying his junk around, and fanning his big head. But I didn't mind it too much. As long as I had some money in my pocket, that was enough. I didn't know the town, I didn't know many people, I didn't know what I wanted to do; but I was happy. I had just turned eighteen and I was free. That lasted about two months.

Then, one night when I was out at work, some man came down the fire-escape of the home on 105th Street, cut the telephone wires, tried to break through the thick, metal bars of my bedroom window, could not, came round to the front, entered the building, ran up the stairs, banged on the door, then started shouting for the girl, who was alone, to let him into the apartment because he wanted to jump her. Nobody in the building interfered; though the noise was enough to wake the dead. After a long while something spooked him and he fled. When I got home late that night the girl was gone. She didn't write a note; the neighbour from across the street had to tell me what happened. I moved out at the end of the month and went to stay with one of the waiters at work. That didn't last too long, either. The man was a homosexual and decided soon after I moved in that I should be his wife. So I moved again and I kept on moving for a long time.

I drifted from one job to the next, one place to the next, leaving the city to live elsewhere, but always returning because it was easy to put some food in my rum belly, a roof over my head, and find a little work when I had to.

I had homes all over town: West Village, the East Side, Chinatown, Midtown. I shared beds, sofas, studios, warehouse floors, offices – whatever came up – until by chance

2

I came to live at a special place, on West 29th Street in Manhattan, where I lived for a long time.

It was September 1987 when I found it. I was waiting to meet a girl who was coming into town for a couple of days from Germany. She worked for the airlines and had a room booked at the Marriott, over in the theatre district. But it was the hurricane season the day she was due in and when I got to her hotel the front desk told me her flight had been delayed three hours by a big storm off the coast of Florida.

I had no money; I could not sit in the bar. I did not want to go back to the place I was living, and I wasn't about to walk the streets in the falling rain, though that neighbourhood – the theatre district, the Port Authority and 42nd Street – is one of my favourite places to stroll. I remembered I knew a newsman whom I had met once in England, many years earlier. He lived somewhere nearby, but for one reason and another I had never managed to go see him. He was a good man; smart, liked to talk, and he moved in a circle much different from my own. As it was a Saturday when this young lady was due, I thought the man would most likely be at home, not at work. I had his address in my book. I decided to go visit.

I left the hotel, loped down past Macy's, then ran when the rains started up again, under the cover of an awning or two, past the Stetson store, to the corner of 29th Street and Broadway.

The architecture on this street wasn't much: the stone buildings were four to five storeys high, dirty, and ornate. But on street level there were show-windows full of fine things to look at: patterned cloths from Africa; jewellery of fake sapphires, rubies and dark wood beads; belts of silver coins; rings, bracelets – all for wholesale, right there in the window to look at, if you wanted.

His building didn't have a number above the door. There was a steep, black, metal staircase leading up to two

3

plain ash-coloured doors at the top. I climbed the stairs, pressed the top bell and when I told him who I was, how we'd met once many years ago and how I happened to be passing by, the door buzzed, not a word having been said.

I pushed and went inside a dark hall. In front was a flight of dusty wood stairs with a chipped bannister. No lights were working on any of the landings above. They were all broken and all the plaster was falling off the walls.

In between the first and the second floor I met a student: glasses, back-pack, and a sour face. He was coming down. I nodded. He didn't say a word.

At the top of the stairs, the newsman was waiting. At first glance he didn't look the type to be a TV reporter. He had on a black bowling shirt with white cowboy piping, black jeans and some black leather shoes with brass buckles which must have been his newsman's shoes. His hair was tousled and long, his clothes unironed, his shoes unpolished. He wasn't Brooks Brothers.

'I think I have just had to interview the worst roommates ever,' he groaned. Then he smiled and offered his hand. 'How would you like a room? The rent is six hundred a month.'

It just so happened I needed a new place to live. I had been staying down in the village but had got involved with my landlady and after too much to drink one night I had made some foolish promises – marriage for one thing, kids for another – in exchange for some free rent because times were tough and I was feeling broody. But the feeling had passed.

And now, just as I was preparing myself to tell the lady I had to go, opportunity had arrived, at six hundred a month, if I wanted it.

I walked in the door of the newsman's home and I knew, almost straight off, it was one of the very best, and just the place for me. It was large by New York standards, run-down, and grand in a fashion of its own. And it had an atmosphere. Friendly.

'I'll take it,' I said.

'You will?' the newsman asked, sounding a little surprised.

'Yes.'

'Don't you think I ought to show you the rest of it first?'

'If you like.'

So he did, and it was all just right, you know. The door opened into a kitchen with a bar area. The ceiling was tall. In the middle, there was a gabled skylight that offered a lot of light, even with the day overcast and stormy like it was. Above the battered wooden bar counter, suspended on chains from the ceiling, were two long wooden planks, stretching the length of the counter, where potted plants wilted.

Everything in the house was run down or falling apart; but the place didn't look precious. People lived in it, which was what I needed after living with this lady who had a place and a way for everything, including what knives to eat breakfast with (different ones from the knives she wanted me to eat my lunch with).

In this kitchen, everything was disposable, or had been disposed of and was currently enjoying a second lease. All of it – the table, the chairs, the crockery, the pans.

'Cable's free,' said the newsman. 'Haven't been charged for the last five years. All the movie channels. MTV. Absolutely free.'

I went over to a tall swing window, behind the kitchen table. Towering above the brick buildings opposite was the Empire State Building: large, keystoning, the top tiers lit red, white and blue; beautiful even in the falling rain. And it was right over the back garden, a giant concrete erection, poking the soft mother sky.

'What a nice thing to see,' I said.

5

'It's not bad, is it?

I was shown the rest of it and it was all eclectic, falling down, falling over, or falling off. The bathroom, just off the kitchen, had an old, green, western bar-style door. I opened it and first thing I saw was a washing machine.

'Doesn't work,' said the newsman. 'Got a dryer, too. Doesn't work either. That fishtank there. Sometimes it works, sometimes it doesn't. Here, let me put the light on so you can see better.'

He went over to the standing lamp on a side table next to the basin; but that didn't work either.

'Needs a new bulb,' said the newsman.

But it was a good bathroom, a place to sit and read for hours whilst taking a soak if there was a bulb.

The newsman's bedroom was in between the kitchen and the main room in front. He showed me it next. The room was large, painted white and had a gabled skylight, fifteen feet up. On one wall hung the American flag. Below was a shabby velvet-covered chaise with cushions. Against one corner was a large double bed with an open book on the pillow. Above it, a gilt-framed oil picture of the Madonna. An old writing table and chair stood to one side. On the far wall was a tall standing cupboard with one of the doors open, some clothes hanging up, and laundry piled high on the floor. The rest of the room was given over to professional stereo equipment and records. Two turn-tables, two cassette decks, two amplifiers, waist-high speakers and maybe a thousand records.

'My vice,' said the newsman. 'Can't stop buying records. Love 'em. Now listen, to get to the front room, where you'll be sleeping, you can either walk through my bedroom, or, go out the front door of the kitchen, then along the hall, and enter the room through a metal door – but don't try closing it. That door has been broken for years.'

We went through. Just inside the door was the platform

6

loft, a ladder climbing up to it. It was above a line of white cupboards, next to a small room that had been partitioned off with sheet-rock. This was where Pedro, the third man to be living in the loft, would kip. But Pedro wasn't around at present.

I climbed the stairs. The ceiling was too low to stand but there was enough space for a double mattress, though not much else. I came down again. I looked over the rest of the room. The newsman went to put on a record.

The wood floor was splintered, there was a bookshelf filled with some classics against one wall, some bad art standing nearby, two old sofas, an armchair, another TV and video, and Pedro's art drawing table in between the two windows looking out down on 29th Street.

'Well?' said the newsman, poking his head around the doorway.

'Best place I've seen in a long time.'

'Good. Welcome.'

That night I was so content I didn't even bother myself with the fact that the young lady who had come across the ocean to visit me had a husband and child back in Germany I hadn't known about before. Nothing could disturb my peace of mind.

But the rent was a problem. Six hundred plus bills is steep. I took off from my roost in the village after two days of drinking whisky, smoking cigarettes and trying to explain things. The lady was not happy with my plan. But she was sort of understanding. 'When you make some money, give me a call, you big bastard,' she said, swinging the door to, after my hefty bag of possessions was flung onto the empty pavement, late one night. I moved uptown, to the West Side. I slept on the floor at an old friend's place and that same week I found myself a job at a pizza restaurant.

The restaurant, the Pizza Palace Restaurant of NYC,

had fica trees, white tiled floors, banquettes, and waiters in goon suits. They sold deep pan pizzas. Not what I wanted, but I was told I'd make good money, so I took it.

September came, I moved in, and all went quite nicely for those first couple of months. I made just about enough to cover the rent and within three days of moving in I met a new girl I fell so in love with I genuinely wanted to marry. I don't know what madness possessed me. She was a Spanish student at NYU. This girl loved to talk about what she was studying and would sit on the floor in the front room and talk for hours about the books she was reading for her English classes. Hesse was her favourite. She liked Salinger, too. We'd make food and she'd talk. Sometimes when I got home late from work, she'd read me things as I sat in the tub waiting for my back rub.

The newsman, though, was a funny man. I said about three words to him. But that was all right, I learnt later: Pedro only said four. The winters affected the newsman's sociable nature. He preferred to lie on his bed, read history books, and listen to music, not sit and talk with us.

One night, not so long after having moved in, I made a great friend, a young Persian called Ramin. I met him in a cheap restaurant over on 14th, a Jamaican place. We were in a group of fifteen and for two hours he was sitting right next to me, ignoring me – ignoring everybody, in fact – not saying a word, looking down at the table, picking at his food. Then, just after the dessert had arrived, he turned to me and said he had designed toilets for a living; but this did not please him much. He wanted to know what I did.

'I wait tables.'

'Does this please you?'

'No.'

'So we have something in common. This is very good.' Then he laughed madly.

Ramin was a thin, dark, charismatic man with a shock

8

of thickly curled black hair and a laugh that could be heard all over Manhattan. Over the next couple of weeks we spent a lot of time walking the streets together, when I wasn't working. He was a three dollar dandy, always put together immaculately, for no money, from the Thrift Stores and the markets in the city. When he came to the loft, he made beautiful drawings and left them as presents. He loved music, Spanish music in particular – he'd always have a tape of the old Flamenco pluckers which he'd put on the moment he arrived. He loved the Spanish girl, and drew her frequently, most of the times naked. He gave me the drawings. I put them on the wall in my loft.

When Ram came over he always showed with a gift, a small beautiful thing he'd found browsing through junk stores. He lived at the Hotel 17, 17th Street, on redundancy checks from the architectural firm he used to work at.

All in all, life had never more pleasant. The girl had her twenty-first in December and we all scoured Canal and Broadway for things to decorate the place with; but then I had to put her on a plane home for Christmas and whilst she was away she had a change of heart. She phoned me on New Year's Eve and told me it was over.

That same afternoon Walter, the General Manager for the restaurant where I worked, called.

'I need you to work tonight,' he said.

'Why?'

'Three servers just called in sick.'

I was not scheduled to work and I did not want to work. It was New Year's Eve. I wanted to kick New Year's Eve in the way everybody else would. But I had rent due the following day and only about four hundred dollars saved. I was hoping to blow some of it on the girl and go late with the rent, but now there was no need, so I said all right to Walt and he said, 'Well, okay, pal. But be there by 4:30, we're going to be busy. Real busy.'

9

We were never real busy. Walt was a born liar and would say anything at all to get a server in for the night if he was short-handed. When I joined I was told I'd average fifty, maybe a hundred dollars a shift. But the truth was, I was lucky to walk with twenty in my pocket after tipping out. Still, it made no difference. I thought a night on the floor with the deep pans might take the mind off things. So I agreed to work.

The rest of that afternoon I half watched one of the bowl games on TV, thought about the girl, and around four got ready to go off to work. When I walked out onto the street with my skate, it was getting dark, and it had just started to snow.

The management of the Pizza Palace Restaurant Co. liked a server to punch in no later than 4:45 for the evening shift. At 4:45 a server was meant to be changed, clocked in, and ready to go out on the floor and make money. This was always impossible and I could never manage it. I rolled through the doors around 4:48 that night, a little out of breath and overheated, and headed for the stairs to the basement. As I bolted past the front reception desk, Mikey, a junior manager of the restaurant, shouted, 'Hey! You're late!'

I ignored him. Everybody did. I ran down the stairs, my skate under my arm, barged through the door marked PRIVATE EMPLOYEES ONLY and headed past the office to the condiment storage room, my private changing area.

In this damp little cave, buried beneath a couple of crates of Coca-Cola concentrate, I kept my Pizza Palace Restaurant Co. server's uniform: a white button down shirt and black polyester slacks.

In the training manual the restaurant gives each server and bar person (a seventy page tome the restaurant asked a server to commit to memory – it was committed for toilet

10

paper at the loft) it stated in italicized print on page two, '*All employees of the Pizza Palace Restaurant Co. are required to wear a clean, white, button-down poly-cotton shirt, with a razor crease in each arm and always have at least two clean shirts ready at any time . . .*'

Page two was the first down the bowl. Being broke I was in no position to afford these two shirts. Razor creases implied the use of an iron. The iron at 29th Street was broken. A second iron cost money. The shirt lived at the restaurant, under the Coca-Cola boxes, next to the cook's pants, beside my Variflex 32″ sports deck with full Trac's and super-hard, free-rolling, lime green Kryptonics of 65mm. That was the best I could do.

I took out my monkey's outfit, put it on, but soon discovered I had a lake of tomato sauce on my chest; and two buttons, between neck and navel, came off in my hand as I was about to fasten them.

I hitched the green, crusty server's apron up around my tits. This fitted both problems and I was ready. It was 4:56.

By 4:57 I was punched in and parched. That night being the Eve, me feeling a little low, I felt it justified and reasonable to have a few drinks whilst I worked the shift. So I went back up the stairs and headed straight for the bar, by the entrance to the restaurant, where Carla the bartender worked. We were friends.

'Hey! You're late!' said young Mikey again, as I appeared on the floor. Again I ignored him; but he was expecting that and rather than make something of it, he let me be. I went past a couple of empty two tops to the long wood bar where Carla had her back to me, writing something by the till.

Carla was born in Vermont and had slept with most of the bartenders on the Upper West Side if the word was to

11

be believed. I got to the bar and she turned and smiled and said, 'How are you?'

'Fine.'

'Good,' she said. 'Would you like a drink?'

'Something strong, please, Carla.'

As she mixed my drink I noticed she was very festive and attractive. A red flower in her hair, pink Chucky Taylor basketball boots (laces undone), a short black mini-skirt that barely covered her belly button, an old school tie loosely knotted between her ample breasts, and an over-sized man's white dress-shirt. Ironed. With a couple of those razor creases. I told her she looked very pretty and she thanked me. She asked what I was doing later, I told her I had no plans. She asked me about my girlfriend. I told her the girl had finished it that afternoon.

'Good,' said Carla. Then she smiled, put my drink up on the bar (it was in a coffee mug. That's how all waiters in the place got stinky) and I took it and headed for the pre-meal in the back room.

The pre-meal was one of Walt's most 'fabulously boring' – the favoured expression of the queens in the place – inventions. It was a pep rally to get us all pumped up to sell! sell! sell! and it was the most tiresome event of the night, on equal par with tallying up the books of cheques, and the money taken from the tables, which we kept in our aprons. Walt started having these pep rallies when he discovered his restaurant was losing money under his great leadership; making a lot less than the last GM. To stimu-late sales Walt tried coupons in the dailies, lunch specials, wine-and-dine specials – he even organized sales compe-titions to see who could, over the period of a month or two, average the highest dollar-per-customer cheque average; but as everyone cheated it didn't mean much when the average soared from seven dollars and change before the competition to the winning average of eight dollars and

12

sixy three cents, by Sal, a method actor, a master of great impressions. The truth was nothing Walt ever tried worked. The rumour circulating the floor was Mikey, the Assistant Manager, the kid with a face the queens said was used in four-wheel drive advertisements – 'They drive over it!' – was being groomed to be the next big pizza. Walt would be shunted off to a siding where he couldn't do any harm; somewhere like a nice mall over in Jersey. And because of all this, Walt figured it was us, the servers, who were fucking his great career in restaurant management. So we had these fifteen-minute pep rallies and team talks to motivate us before each shift. But it was the same old crap each time and worth missing if it didn't get you fired.

I tooled around the corner into the back room, whistling, about fifteen minutes late now, feeling just a little bit better with the booze on board, and Walt nailed me.

'You're late!' he shouted, jabbing a stubby finger at his fake Cartier wrist-watch.

I complained about the traffic.

'But you're on a skateboard fahchrissakes!'

Now here I was presented with a difficult problem. I could lie (the snow, had to rescue some kids caught on the ice in Central Park, etc) – which I do all the time with these boys; without guilt, too – but the truth was I didn't give two shakes if I stayed or was chucked. Part of it was because I wasn't feeling so bright, and a part of it was because this is one of the rare luxuries of having a bum job. The job goes nowhere. By walking out the door (or being thrown out, depending on circumstance) I was never plagued by the feeling I had just passed up the greatest opportunity of my life, the one that would keep me in food and rent for as long as I chose – not that I knew what that felt like, but I was sure it had got to be bad.

With nothing better to do, I yawned.

13

'Oh,' said Walt sarcastically, 'am I boring you? Ohh! I'm *so* sorry. Really.'

I didn't bother to answer. Everything about Walt irritated me: his pudgy face, his pudgy manner, his whining voice, his desperate pride in his little pizza restaurant and its place in the fine dining world of the city. It all seemed a little pointless. This was only pizza we were selling here. Not a cure for cancer. Eventually, after glaring at me long and hard, he sighed deeply, rolled his hog's slits and said, 'Now, where was I?'

Though I had not been sitting there for the last fifteen minutes, I knew exactly where Walt was. Walt was where he always was after fifteen minutes of a pre-meal: step six or step seven of the *Pizza Palace Nine Steps To Perfect Service*! This was the server's gospel (pages forty-one to sixty-eight in the manual), delivered at the start of every shift, without fail. I kept my mouth shut. As nobody else seemed to be listening either, Walt said, 'Hmm. Well I'll tell you what we'll do. For the benefit of those of us who were late – ' All eyes on me. A derisive hoot from the queens. ' – let me go over it once more, okay?'

And since no one had the sense to tell him to can it, Walt started over from the beginning.

'Okay, step one: ID the customer. Approach the table and smile! Then say, "Hi, how ya doin' today? My name is Walter. I'm gonna be the server for your delicious meal tonight!"

'Next, drop a bev nap in front of each new customer. Ask the gentleman or the lady if they would like to order a cocktail. Say, "Sir, can I get you a cocktail while you look at the menu?" No, Walter? "Okay, okay – how 'bout a bottle of wine?" And remember, servers! A bottle of wine can add ten dollars to your cheques . . .'

A bottle of wine can do that, of course, but with the evening being the Eve, and my heart feeling ruined, I felt

14

it would have a better use sitting in my belly fermenting my vision. But I said nothing. I didn't want to go out into the cold on my board and head home just yet. I always think it best to get the rent covered before you get the can, if you can manage it.

So Walt droned on, skipping about the tables where we all sat, ten of us for the night shift, illustrating the finer points of good service, squealing with delight with each success he had at selling his imaginary customer whatever item he cared to unload – garlic bread, salads, wines, beers, desserts, coffee – until finally, just as I was about to fall asleep, he said, 'So there you have it, my friends. Nine steps to perfect service! *Nine steps to heaven.* Thank you for your patience. Now let's all go out there, and *let's make money!*'

'O-kay!' we all yelled, stamping from the tables. I headed for the bar leaving Walt and Mikey in the back room inspecting the tables for place settings and full salt and pepper shakers.

'Another please,' I said to the lovely Carla, who was, no doubt about it, going to get lovelier all night.

'Are you going to get drunk?' she asked me, giggling.

'I hope so.'

Tables arrived. The restaurant filled. By 7:30 the whole place was full and I wanted to break Johnny's big fat neck. Johnny was the host for the night, a muscle nut of Puerto-Rican and Polish blood, with the face of a ship-builder from Gdansk drilled once too often by a rivet gun. He was the man responsible for seating the customers; he was a hipster with downtown clothes and a downtown attitude which meant he didn't say a word. He had skull rings, a pony-tail, shoes from Trash & Vaudeville, a gold cap for his front tooth, and the physique of a Mack truck. As long as you didn't touch his butt (the homosexuals were always pinching it), he was all right. But that night he seemed to have it in for me. Not only had he given me tables – which

15

I did not want, preferring to concentrate on the liquor – but also he had given me table after table of kids.

Problem with kids is they all want Shirley Temples. A Shirley Temple requires a trip to the bar at the front of the restaurant, for grenadine. A trip to the bar from my slot in the back room was a two-minute hike through busy restaurant traffic with a bar tray of tall glasses that had a nasty habit of falling over and smashing everywhere. A server did not want to go anywhere near the bar at that particular time of the evening, with the restaurant packed, unless someone had ordered a whole slew of expensive drinks, or, more importantly, the server's mug of booze was finished and needed refilling – which mine did; but with Walt prowling the joint, probably sniffing every empty coffee mug, I felt it would have to wait a while.

'No Shirley Temples,' I told a table of screaming brats.

One of the kids – there's always one – didn't believe me.

'Ma! Ma!' he bawled. 'This guy says there's no Shirl . . .'

I laid a firm hand on the young fella's shoulder and whispered in his ear. 'If you're quiet, junior, I'll give you ice-cream. Free. How 'bout that?'

Kids, in my experience, are suckers for bribes with the ice-cream.

'I don't want ice-cream! I wanna Shirley Temple!' he screamed.

I fetched the little man a Shirley Temple. I fetched them all Shirley Temples and I fetched one for myself, too, laced with vodka. Somehow, I can't figure how, the little man ended up getting my Shirley Temple, and when they left the place a while later he was running around the floor telling everyone what a good pizza he had just eaten.

Now, when deep in the weeds – as I seemed to be shortly afterwards – the *Nine Steps To Perfect Service* are reduced by necessity to three. Step One: Take an order. Step Two: Give 'em food. Step Three: Drop the cheque and tell 'em to get lost. However, this only works well when you don't have a difficult and demanding customer. I had one, and it was a lady, and she had been waving at me for about fifteen minutes now, if I had cared to think about it, which I tried not to.

Thing to do when people start waving at you, is run. That way, they can't distract your attention. And if you happened to be wanting to focus it all on the exciting all-new portfolio of swimsuits and lingerie of the prettiest waitress/model on the floor, this is what a waiter must do.

'Wha'd'ya think?' this girl Cindy, who wanted to be a fashion model, asked me.

Cindy had all the bells and whistles. I had had a crush on her for the whole time I worked at the restaurant; but as I had been in love with the Spanish girl I had never tried to pursue it. Cindy came from Utah, was a blonde, wore crisp, white shirts and little velvet things in her hair that she bought from the street vendors on Broadway, pleated, short, black tennis skirts and was nice, too. Never had a bad word to say about anybody.

'Well, what d'you think?' she asked me again as I stared at these handsome pictures.

I told her she was gorgeous, that I could just tell, by the way she posed, she had a natural flair for the dramatic. She had all the signs of becoming an actress. A great one.

'How did you know I wanted to act?' she asked me.

'Intuition,' I said. 'A face like yours . . . As a matter of fact, I study the drama.'

'You do? I didn't know that!'

Me neither. But I'd say anything for a kiss from a pretty girl like her when feeling so depressed.

'Yes,' I said, 'I do. And for quite some time now. Acting is one of the great arts, in my opinion. Actors and actresses are my favourite people. They're so real, d'you know. I just love them.'

'Me too.'

But at that moment I had to put the sluice gate down and skedaddle over to my table where Walt was fast approaching the woman who had been waving all this time.

'Is everything under control?' Walt asked me as I sailed past.

'Absolutely,' I replied, putting my ship in reverse and docking alongside, trying to look sober. 'This lady is having three, ah, Spinnocolis, a Four Seasons and a, ah, um. Table twenty-seven are so happy. Table twenty-eight is . . .'

I walked off thumbing a number of my cheques, looking busy.

Walt bought it, though. He went back to the reception desk to welcome new customers as I went over to the lady's table.

'Now, Ma'am,' I said. 'What would you like? The cheque, maybe?'

'A dessert.'

Desserts are a pain to make. Best thing to do when a customer asks for a dessert is to sell 'em garlic bread. Garlic bread is easy to make.

'I don't want garlic bread,' the lady told me. 'I want a dessert.'

'Don't have 'em.'

'What d'you mean you don't have them? It says right here on the . . .'

I took the menu out of her paw. Time for another mug full. When I got back all the lady wanted was the cheque, which was a good thing because that was all she was going to get. She gave me money and I gave her change for a ten.

'But I gave you a twenty,' the lady said.

'No you didn't.'

'Get me the manager!'

The truth was I didn't know what she had given me and

18

didn't really care. I knew I didn't want Walt within spitting distance of me. So I gave her change for a twenty and was glad to see the back of her and her Bergdorf shopping bags.

But then a problem. On the way back through the restaurant, with a new coffee mug full of booze, I saw Walt standing around to see if he could see signs of me. I went to the men's room. I stayed there for about fifteen minutes. Walt got me when I got back up on the floor.

'What's wrong with you?'

I hiccuped.

'I want to see you down in my office in five minutes, all right?'

Not really. I got Nick, one of the nicest homosexuals in the place, to cover for me, sucked down a couple of cokes and headed for the basement, prepared for the worst.

'Are you not feeling well?' Walt asked me, when I closed the door. He sounded concerned.

'I got the flu.'

'Listen, I had a call from some lady who came in earlier tonight with a group of four kids. She said you were her waiter. D'you know the one I'm talking about?'

'I think so.'

'She says her son won't sit still for a minute, runs around the apartment hunting the family cat, trying to put the animal in the tumble dryer. And when he's not doing that he keeps laughing and yelling at his Ma to bring him some more pizza. She says she doesn't know what's got into him. Do you know anything about this?'

'No.'

'It sounds to me like he's drunk.'

'I gave them all Shirley Temples.'

'Maybe the kid had a reaction to something he ate.'

'I believe he must've.'

'All right. Well, hang in there, buddy. I can't let you go;

19

but I had to ask. The woman is going to call back in a few minutes.'

'No problem, Walt. Glad to be of assistance.'

So I had a reprieve and only one table left. I went back to the floor, filled up my coffee mug and went to the back of the restaurant, to the bus station, where all the servers gathered to smoke and gossip.

Young Billy, a budding actor who always sang Steven Sondheim show tunes when he worked the floor, was suicidal. His younger boyfriend, a spotty kid that used to come to the restaurant each day at the end of Billy's shift to pick him up, had announced that day he was leaving him, for good.

'Who for?' I asked.

'A woman!'

At that moment, Mikey came purposefully over to ask why we were laughing, and why, more importantly, weren't we looking after our tables, like we should be?

All coffee mugs were slung into the bus trays.

Mikey reminded us that as servers of The Pizza Palace Restaurant Co., we should take note of page fifty-three in the training manual and if we did, we would see that all servers when not checking their tables should be checking to see if the salad station or bus stations were properly stocked with napkins, sugars, sweet'n'lows, glasses etc.

'Nice buns,' said Nick, studying young Mikey's butt.

'And doesn't Mary wiggle them fabulously!' trilled Henri, another waiter, dancer and great smoker. Mikey blushed and walked away.

I went to the bar. Billy went to get changed. When he was done he came over. Carla had just told me she was free for a night and thought we ought to go out and do something together, like each other. Billy said, 'Good night, friends. Happy New Year.' It was the flattest Happy New Year I'd ever heard.

'Where are you going?' I asked him.

'Times Square. To watch the count.'

'Why don't you stay with us?'

He didn't want to stay. We watched him disappear into the snow and the crowds on Columbus. The restaurant was now almost empty, the rush had finished everywhere but my nut, which was pickled in the restaurant's most useful liquors. By this hour I was almost fully incapacitated and quite a mess, I'll say.

At ten-to-twelve, with Walt tucked away in his office in the basement, fretting over sales figures comparisons over the years, the restaurant's radio was tuned to KISS FM. Someone pumped up the volume and Lois, a nice guy who washed the dishes, appointed himself the lighting expert for the night and started flashing the lights on and off, in time to the beat. The busboys, Enrique, Manolo and Juan, made a human chain and started to dance between the empty tables, some with the chairs up on top.

I locked the doors. The count started. Then Mikey appeared and, seeing us all fooling around, put his hands on his hips, disgusted, and said, 'You guys are so unprofessional!'

'Yeah!' I felt obliged to shout.

'Abtholutely!' said Lois, clapping his hands.

I joined the busboys. Carla joined me. I fell over. Carla fell over. The whole line fell over and laughed. About ten minutes after that Walt accused me of being drunk, when I couldn't tally my cheques. I congratulated him on his keen powers of observation.

'You're drunk?' he asked me, half astounded, half furious.

'Extremely.'

'You're fired!'

'Thank you.'

This was one of the jobs when I was bodily evicted from the premises. But I didn't care.

The rest of that night, Carla and I skated around the bars of the Upper West Side, two-up on my skateboard, riding through the snow, having a great time. We hopped from one place to another, drinking free because she knew all the bartenders. That Carla – she had the tongue of a six-foot lizard.

Just after four in the morning, when we were on our way back up to her place on Amsterdam, we found a kitten on the street. We heard it as we passed, so we stopped.

'Probably belongs to that kid,' I said.

'Which kid?'

'The one who got my drink.'

The kitten walked over to where we were standing.

'It's a good luck charm,' said Carla. 'You have to rescue it.'

'I don't like cats.'

'You have to rescue it,' Carla said. She picked it up and put it in my arms. 'There! You see? She loves you. And if you don't take her, she'll probably die.'

'Why don't you take it?'

'Not allowed animals in my building.'

So I took it and stuck it in my coat. Poor thing was half frozen to death. Then the three of us skated slowly up Amsterdam Avenue.

When we got to her building, an old run-down place that used to be a welfare hotel, we snuck the cat past the doorman, took it up to her room and gave it some milk. We lit a fire and it went fast to sleep. We went to bed soon afterwards. On New Year's Day I took it home with me to live with the boys on 29th Street.

Two

It was many months into the New Year when I got a call from an old friend in England with an offer to pluck me out of Manhattan, 29th Street, my cat, a number of bad jobs and the news that the Spanish girl had got married that March, and not to me.

My friend was a career man and had great ambition for lucre. At the age of twenty-seven, he had a house, a sports car, and a farm in the south of England. This was commendable in my eyes, considering the difficulties I always experienced when trying to cover the rent. For years I had not heard a word from him. Then all of a sudden he calls up and tells me he's had enough of his job, is going to quit, and wants to know what I think about this foolishness.

'What,' I asked, 'is going on with your head?'

Ah, many changes, he said. Many changes. He told me he no longer enjoyed getting up and going to work in the City of London. It didn't make him happy. And anyway, London was full of bastards. Work bastards, cocktail bastards, pub bastards – this was no way to live a life. For what? he asked me. A hundred-and-fifty-thousand measly dollars a year?

I had my share of bastards to deal with, too. The landlord, for example. During the day the man filled himself with drugs and snapped calender photographs of young girls in string-bikinis in his studio, three floors below. But at night his drug-taking made him a crazy man. One night in February he woke the whole building with gunfire, claiming to have taken a pot-shot at some thief. There was no thief. Another night, not so long after, he stumbled into the apartment at four in the morning and woke us all up. He'd come to read our toes, he said. The toe-reading was to make sure we were good for the month. He said he was fed up collecting late rent. We were too dazed to argue; but when the toes were put up on the table he did offer an explanation: he was now a warlock, warlocks could see these things in toes. So we showed him them, and the toes were fat with promise, which was news to us, of course. Satisfied, he then left us, probably to go and disturb one of the other tenants.

With the sort of money my friend made, I could get the fat man to come into the apartment each morning, spread some of his special witches' dust on the mess that is our home, stir my bubble bath with his broomstick, warm my toilet seat with his hairy cheeks, and never disturb us. And here was my friend about to give it all up.

'Why?' I asked him.

'Going to buy a boat and sail around the world,' he said. 'Do the planet.'

'Well,' I said, without a moment's hesitation. 'Let me come, too, please.'

'That's why I was calling. I need a hand taking the boat across the Atlantic. You're the only person I could think of who doesn't have a real job.'

'That's true.'

'So, what about it? The Trades in November. One of the great sleigh rides on the world's oceans. Think of it. A roller-coaster.'

Months in an amusement park. I immediately saw great promise. Skip winter in New York City, skip wearing bin-liner in my sneakers, skip the abuse when washing the windscreens of hostile car and truck drivers down on Houston for the extra Christmas pennies. Skip it all. For a ride on a puff-powered Winnebago.

'All right, I'm in,' I said.

'You'll do it?'

'I'm your man.'

So for the next ten minutes we talked about this once in a lifetime opportunity to escape from the worries of normal living; to be out there on the ocean with the birds and the fish. As we talked my pulse quickened and my face spread into a crooked smile the size of his bank account. But right at the end of the conversation, just as I was getting highly adjusted to the idea, my friend said, 'And you know what? It'll be a chance *to find ourselves, matey!*'

'A chance to what?'

'Find ourselves!'

He told me what he wanted to do was get in touch with something called the self. The bank's loot had buried it somewhere, and the sea, he felt, was the only place to retrieve it; scrub clean the soul; purge himself of bad habits; be true once more to the word of the Good Book – for my friend was a devout Catholic and took the Church to heart. That's how he put it. I felt he probably just wanted to have some fun, sleep late, and see something more pretty than his old boss in the elevator each morning. But I didn't care what his reasons might be – it's not often a man like me is offered such a unique opportunity in life. A noble deck hand. It was an offer like dinner: too good for a man to refuse.

'Got any money?' my friend asked.

'Nope.'

'I can't afford to pay you a penny.'

All great adventures in life start under these difficult circumstances.

*

Months later, at the beginning of the fall, having quit another job and rented my room at 29th Street to a film student for four months, I left for England. Carla came to the airport with me, on the bus.

'Are you going to stay faithful to me while you're gone?' she asked.

'I don't know.'

'Doesn't matter, anyway,' said Carla.

'Would you keep an eye on the cat? Please?'

'I will. Be careful.' Then she kissed me, smiled, turned and headed across the concourse to get the bus back into the city.

In my pocket I had some money saved from working two shifts, seven days a week, at another food emporium. But it wasn't much and aeroplane drinks are expensive. I checked in. I flew. The following day I met my pal on the quay on the south coast of England, in the rain.

He is a big, funny man, with a face like an eagle and a body like an old grizzly. He was an ex-rugby player, could tell a great story and was looking very pleased when we hugged. The boat was a wood yawl, forty-two feet, and it sat in thick black mud ten feet from where we met.

He was so excited and he told me everything he'd learnt. He told me the yacht was a winner of the Bermuda Race in 1964; it was built by Germans in the Bremen yard; it was a yawl of the finest pedigree and design – the Sparkman & Stephens firm of New York City.

The list of this little yacht's accomplishments was endless. But the important points were these: she was made back in 1962; and she was small, forty-two feet.

Barbados is many thousands of miles over the ocean from the south coast of England. No doubt some of this would be rough. Now a sleigh ride – that's what he had called it – across the heaving Atlantic in December would put a lot of stress on an old vessel like this.

'Does it float?' I asked.

'She's a blue water boat,' my friend said stiffly. 'An ocean crosser. A heavy-weather boat. She can take it all right. And she's a dry boat. That's right, a dry boat – not like that Oyster . . .'

We had both sailed together years before on a yacht that leaked. I believed every yacht leaked. This is what I told him.

'You don't know what you're talking about,' he said.

It was my firm belief no vessel made of wood could keep water out; like no old motor-cycle could keep oil in. It was a law of nature. So we squabbled, and I was informed that not only did I not know what I was talking about but also I lacked sensitivity.

Long days and nights had been invested in the preparation of the boat for this great voyage. Months of labour and sacrifice, he told me, with no help from anyone but young Tobin, the third hand, a volunteer my friend had found in some pub in North Cornwall. The boat was sound, sturdy, dry and his baby. Apologize, bastard, he said.

I did. I suggested we might repair the slight with a large number of drinks at the local watering hole, stocked well with strong beer and pretty, rosy-cheeked teenage girls.

'Do you realize how much work there is to be done on board?' I was asked.

'But this is a holiday,' I reminded him.

'This is *not* a holiday.'

And the man was right. From that moment on the weekend became a week day. Supplies were loaded, the galley scrubbed, the lites polished, the shrouds taped, the shackles wired – it was nonstop, until ten every night. Two days and two nights we worked with Tobin, a man I had not met before.

Tobin was a Cornishman, a lifeguard, a cook, a surfer, and according to the boss and himself, catnip to women.

27

He was twenty years old. For the last two months he had helped prepare the boat, living on my friend's farm. He always smiled, was quick with jokes, though when I first met him he was a little shy. But he never once complained.

Not me. This scrubbing and cleaning was not what I had come for. I had had hopes of spending the weekend tacking around the bar and beating up to as many nice English girls as possible for some friendly conversation. But when we finally got the chance to drop anchor and let loose the sheets and sink the large quantity of drinks I had been anticipating, it was just before we were due to sail.

The skipper was out in the beer garden with all the friends he'd invited down to see him off, when a man came over and sat next to me at the bar.

'You're on the boat,' he said to me. 'Aren't you?'

I told him I was.

'Thought so! Care for a drink?' He ordered two pints. 'Going through Biscay, eh?'

'That's right.'

'Want to get through there as quickly as possible, old boy. Otherwise . . .' And he made a face like he had just seen a ghost. 'The Equinox gales! Wreck an old boat like that!'

'Is that so?' I said.

'Terrible place!'

He introduced himself giving a name I missed, but he told me he was something to do with the skipper, so I assumed he probably knew what he was talking about with matters of the sea. In this little town and particularly at this bar, in the Sailing Club, everybody was a sailor of yachts, and therefore much better qualified to understand the difficulties of the passages ahead of us than me, an expert with the oars on the lake in Central Park, in the middle of Manhattan.

I started to drink. He nudged me. 'Let's hope it's not

28

your last, what? Couldn't have picked a worse time to go across if you tried. Why, your continental shelf – there's a graveyard! Waves the size of seasoned oaks swamp vessels! Snap 'em in half! Dearie, dearie me, what a dreadful place! S'pose no one told you about the old shelf, eh? Probably didn't want you to worry. Still, what I always say is *best the devil you know*, eh? Your continental shelf! Now there's a place you want to avoid like the pox!'

The shelf, he claimed, lay underwater in the Bay, and shallowed the Atlantic rollers as they came in. In a storm – of which there were many at this time of year, he was happy to tell me – towering waves of white water were thrown up to swamp little boats of forty-two feet and send men to their doom.

'Just thought you ought to know, old boy,' he said. 'Your round, I believe.'

Shortly afterwards the skipper came in through the lunch crowd in his Guernsey and boat shoes and ochre shorts and said we were going, the tide was high.

'See you in Barbados, then!' said the man waving from his stool at the bar as I left. 'Be down there myself at Christmas. Have a few rum punches if you make it! And by the way . . .' I was almost outside. '. . . watch out for those tanker johnnies! Your tanker johnny is either asleep at the wheel, or *drunk*! They *never* see boats as small as yours!'

Out in the beer garden I told my friend about the conversation. He said, 'Oh, don't listen to him. The man doesn't know what he's talking about. His idea of sailing is sitting on a gin palace moored in Monte Carlo. He's teasing.'

Six days later as the barometer fell, the wind rose, the seas worsened, and the skipper had just thrown up over the lee winches, I mentioned the man in the bar and he said, 'Right, I think we'll tack. You're on the winches.'

The skipper had become a sparring partner. Some of this was caused by frustration with the boat. She was, as my friend had said, a blue water boat; only the water was on the inside as well as the outside: we had a leak.

And some of it was caused by the stress and duress the old goat suffered having left England on a voyage that would probably take him two years, with a crew of novices, on a boat that was leaking, in a sea of water with a notorious reputation. But this was not my concern. I was on holiday. I wanted him to put a smile on his whiskered mug. So we had our little disagreements. But the other two, Chris and Tobin, they were princes.

Near eight in the morning, the seventh day out of port, the sky overcast, thirty-five knots of wind coming over a short sea and the decks. The boss looked at me as I stood in the hatchway out of the wind having a quiet snooze, and said from his post behind the wheel, 'Time for breakfast. You're cooking today.'

This cooking at sea was the first true test of the business of finding yourself. If you could cook a meal without finding yourself throwing up all over it, you were doing better than most. The kitchen was a hell-hole. Not only did the floor behave like it was a wall, but the food refused to stay put for longer than a blink of an eye. Eggs scrambled themselves by jumping out the bowl and exploding on the cabin sole. Packs of streaky bacon flew around the cabin like frightened swine as we were smacked by one large wave and thumped by the next. The real trouble with the galley was it wasn't designed by a fetishist. The proprietor of a XXXX video, magazines, novelties and rubber goods store would cut-to-fit counters of black rubber for the galley, making it safe, interesting and practical. I told the skipper this just after a can of tomatoes caught me smack on the temple.

'You don't know what you're talking about,' he said.

So we squabbled about that, too. The genius that designed our pokey ship's galley put a lip on the counters for food restraint – which is fine as long as there is rubber and not 15-year-old linoleum to slide on – in which case the lip became a launch ramp and pesky cans of tomatoes started behaving like artillery shells. And that was before getting near the stove.

The stove would have been arrested if it hadn't been on the boat. Swinging around on gimbals, the thing had the instincts of a hooligan and smacked this cook in the kidneys each time his fingers were burnt trying to light it. All in all, cooking sucked. But I did it and I delivered it proudly to the boys: fried eggs, bacon, beans, boiled tomatoes and toast. A feast.

'Not for me,' said the skipper as I held a plastic plate out the open hatch for him.

'Why not?'

'Not hungry, actually. Hmm, always lose my appetite when we first put to sea.'

This, then, was the only advantage so far of being at sea. My pal, who normally had the appetite of an aircraft carrier, could not eat a morsel because he felt sick. All the more for us. But then a wave broke down the decks. His breakfast went overboard before I could get my mouth into it. 'As I have told you,' said the boss, grinning, 'at sea you must be aware of what is going on round you.'

Next, the washing up. This also sucked. Trying to free bacon grease and burnt oats is hard enough in a sink with warm water; but when the floor is moving, the water is freezing, and a hundred gallons of cold sea-water is making a bee-line for the back of the neck each time the hull crashes through a wave (you have to lean out the open hatch to do this foolish chore) is fiercely unpleasant. This might have put me in a mood if it were not that I remembered this journey was an odyssey: a test of character, resolve and personality. I mentioned this.

'Can't fuck character,' said the skipper. I emptied a load of sea-water out of my shirt, onto the cockpit floor.

'I can,' shouted young Tobin from his bunk. 'And personality, too.'

Tobin, the ship's scribe, known as Homer the dyslexic, very bright, the best cook aboard (he was bribable, too), spent all his free time in his bunk composing long letters to his girl, at home in Boscastle, North Cornwall. This girl got about thirty pages a day out of him, as he monitored all conversations from his bunk.

After the washing up, I changed and went up on deck. This was the only place to go if you didn't want to be sick. For a couple of hours we sat and smoked. Then near lunch that day the skipper informed us we were coming up on Ushant. Ushant was a large malevolent lump of black-faced rock, shrouded in heavy mist, with a tall breaking sea on the shore, which we could hear miles off. This, according to the charts, was the beginning of Biscay. On this island was a weather station. The weatherman's forecast on the VHF would determine if we would continue, or run somewhere safe, like a bar in a port. The skipper went down below to talk to him.

A fair to moderate sea was reported by the weatherman, 20–25 knots of wind, no storm warnings, no high winds, no depressions. Biscay was as calm as it would ever be. That was the promise.

'Can't trust the weatherman,' said the skip. 'Look what happened during the Fastnet in '79. I think we ought to consider going to Brest.'

We had other ideas. Chris, being part-owner, was spokesman. We wanted to get somewhere where it was warm. So far, the only good times on the boat were when we were moored up in port, drinking late into the night, arguing about absolutes like whether the skip had to cook. We had long, howling conversations about absolutes.

The boss listened, went below to study his barometer, did not like what he saw, but agreed to continue.

That afternoon something good happened. The boss exhausted himself behind the wheel, sapped by tiredness, lack of nourishment and the cold. This was good because, when he finally keeled over and was put in his bunk with a plastic mug of tea, he was so tired and cold we didn't hear one word of complaint or insult out of him for a good many hours.

However, he was still our skipper. There to inspire us to great deeds, like cooking. When he woke in the early evening, still cold, tired, damp and sea-sick, I asked my friend for a joke.

'Bugger off,' he replied from his bunk, shivering.

'I'll tell you something funny then,' I said from my spot, strapped into the stove and the sauté pans.

'What?'

'My turn to drive soon.'

'Oh, God.'

In this sea, which was short and rough, the boss didn't want me anywhere near the wheel. Driving a sail-boat was a skilful occupation. It took years to become an ace. I felt I could get the knack of it quick and had been pleading for a shot behind the wheel ever since we had pulled away from the quay in England. But there had always been a good reason why I shouldn't – I was irresponsible and a danger to everyone, was the skipper's favourite.

That first night in Biscay, heading due west under a moonless sky, in a growing sea, Chris and the boss took it in turns through the night at the wheel. The weather worsened and the seas grew. By the following morning the boss ship-wrecked. He crawled into his damp bunk, cursing our bad luck and the foul weather.

But I was excited. At last it was my turn to drive. If trouble came, as we were now almost sure it would according to the falling barometer on the wall of the heads below, the boys needed to be rested up and able-bodied. Taking the wheel for the first time, the only thing I was instructed to do was steer a course of 270 degrees, due west. We needed sea-room in case we were pushed east by the storm.

Almost immediately it came to me that the best way to pilot this ship through the short, rough sea was to treat the sea like a mogul field. In no time I had the yacht leaping out the water like a little fish. I was having a fine time, too, until the hatch suddenly was slung back and a horrible, wild-eyed, screaming, wet head poked out into the wind and started bawling.

'*Who d'you think you are?*' the skipper shouted, white with rage. '*Errol fucking Flynn?*'

At the time, I was standing behind the wheel, hair blowing in the breeze, watchman's cap over one eye, a boot up on the windward locker, squinting at the blow and the ocean spray. This was the best position to see over the decks at the launch ramps as they came into position beneath my bows. I was not sitting sedately as the boss did.

'You're meant to steer *around* the fucking waves,' the boss shouted. 'Not *over* them!'

I did not enjoy it so much after that.

The rest of the day passed uncomfortably. The skipper was confined to bunk with exhaustion, Tobin reeled off another twenty pages to his girl in Boscastle and Chris and I sat on the wet deck, in the wind and cold ocean spray, yapping about this and that and getting very crafty at

34

smoking damp cigarettes that fell apart after a couple of drags.

Next day the barometer fell further, and the sea shortened and heightened dramatically. The man in the bar must have known something. The sea was just like he said it would be. Big and wicked.

After lunch, the wind blew constant at 45 knots. The one advantage of 45 knots of wind is you can't hear a word the skipper says when he's shouting and you're hanging on to the boom which is skimming a couple of feet above a rough, grey sea, whilst trying to put a reef in the main that won't do what it's supposed to. All you hear is the howling wind and all you see is a gnashing jaw at the wheel. This is the only way to sail if skipper is feeling poorly.

We spent an hour climbing around pulling at things, getting cold and wet. When the sails were down, bagged, thrown in the sail lockers in the cockpit, then replaced with smaller storm canvas, we sat on wet cushions and drank tea. Tea was good for morale. As morale was doing no better than the boat, we drank lots of tea.

'Always thought I'd see my arse in Biscay,' the boss muttered to no-one in particular as we sat watching the windspeed indicator go shooting up the clock.

'Here,' said Tobin, passing me his camera. 'Take a picture of me for mum and Karen, will you?'

Tobin's picture was snapped in a variety of heroic poses. Then the boat was battened down for a storm.

'If we turn turtle,' the boss said when done, 'just pray we come up again.'

'Buggered?' Tobin asked from his bunk. 'One "t" or two?'

Late that afternoon we learnt from the BBC shipping forecast that a storm Force 10 had now formed in the Irish Sea and was moving south towards Biscay. The wind was strengthening. The sea was changing up from bungalow size to three- and four-storey size.

As nightfall approached, the skipper shared with us another worry he thought we ought to be aware of. 'Containers – they're bastards. They come off container ships in big storms and float a few feet beneath the surface.'

'What happens if we hit one of them?' I asked.

'Probably sink. Just like if the hatch goes. If the hatch goes we're finished. Now whose turn is it to make some tea?'

That night, because the sea was so big, we had a new watch system. Instead of having just one man on deck per watch, we had two – one to steer the boat, and one to look behind at the great bubbling slopes and valleys of dark water as they rushed down on the stern.

I went to my wet bunk that night shortly after dinner and thought about nice, warm places. I thought about 29th Street where it was warm and the bed didn't move. I thought about Carla and I thought about walking into a bar and having a drink. I tried to sleep; but I couldn't. I kept expecting the boat to tip over and sink.

From time to time I could hear the boss shout up on deck and the grinding sound of a winch tightening up a sheet. Sometimes I could hear the slush of water as a wave broke over the boat and ran down over the decks. Now and then I'd hear the boss shout, 'Come up! Come up!' above the roar of the wind and feel the boat suddenly get picked up and carried down the face of a large, breaking wave. After an hour of listening to all this I then heard water slopping about on the cabin sole. I fell out of my bunk and went to the pump at the navigator's table. The cabin sole was swilling with sea-water. I pumped and Chris pumped and after fifteen minutes the bilges were empty and the sea-water on the cabin sole was gone. But I didn't sleep. I kept thinking the little tub would tip over and sink.

36

Near twelve that night, I got up to put on my foul weather gear for the night watch. This was a good name. It had been foul for the last three days. And since the clothes lockers were now swilling about with sea-water, there was nothing dry aboard to wear, either, after a watch.

'Got a joke for you, mate,' Chris said.

After a struggle with life vest, a trip on the ten-foot lifeline and a fall into the swill of sea-water on the cabin sole, I got up.

'What's that?' I asked.

Chris was flung into the clothes locker. He came out with his sea boots, and giggled. He climbed around the cabin table to sit on the bunk as the boat pitched steeply down another wave. He put on his sea boots and told me his joke:

Three missionaries caught in the jungle by a bunch of cannibals are given the choice of death or Bunda. The first two take Bunda and discover that this Bunda is a gang sodomy. The last missionary says he'll take death thinking he'll avoid this Bunda'ing. But the chief smiles and tells him, 'Death – by Bunda!'

Considering our current circumstance this Bunda joke seemed most appropriate. The whole trip had been nothing but a long Bunda. The boat was sinking, it was starting to blow very hard, and we were tired, wet, cold and hungry. And this was a holiday, too. Without pay. I laughed and laughed.

When we were ready I opened the hatch. Just at that same time a wave hit the bow and smashed on the cabin roof, sending cold sea-water spilling down the open hatch, and down the back of my neck.

'That,' said Christopher, 'is another Bunda, mate.'

Soon after, the boss gave us the signal – 'Hurry up or we'll all fucking sink' – and we clambered out the hatch

37

into the cold night, clipped the lifelines to the deck wires, bolted the hatch, and sat on wet cushions in the cockpit, waiting for the eyes to acclimatize themselves. It was very cold. The surrounding sea had grown but it was difficult to determine by how much since it was so dark. Enough wind to uproot trees showed on the wind-speed indicators. There were no stars, no moon, the cloud cover was low, and it was almost pitch black; but the boat's motion felt more regular now that we were up on deck.

Minutes later, their watch done, Tobin made coffee. The skipper put on a tape, and turned up the volume. The deck speakers pumped out music louder than the howl of the storm and a strange turnaround moment occurred. Coming when we were tired, cold, and worried, the music was a feast. It lifted the damp spirit. Suddenly, sitting on a wet deck, in wet clothes, in the cold, swamped by a big sea, in the middle of a howling gale, with my friend, was a grand place to be. I would not have wanted to be anywhere else, not Carla's bed, nowhere. We shared a couple of cigarettes, the first hour passed and I was the eyes. As tall waves came rushing down at the stern, I called course. The long surfs down the white water saw the boat-speed indicator show twelve, thirteen, fourteen knots. And in theory the boat was capable of going no faster than eight. But then, just as we were about to switch, we saw lights.

The trouble with lights is they come with ships. Ships in this bay were full of sleeping fools, or drunks, if the man in the bar was to be believed, and there was no reason why he shouldn't be. I saw two white lamps lined up, one on top of the other, a red lamp to the right, a green lamp to the left pointing straight at us.

Fifteen minutes later they were closer. Another ten minutes, the lights lined up and pointed at the beam a little aft of the cabin. This made me more nervous than the weather, the leak, and all of the skipper's doomy prophecies.

38

To change course, now that we were running with the predominant swells of the big sea behind us, would risk taking it broad-side and the chance of a capsize and a night in the icy water.

I went down the pitching decks to the mast to see if the running lamps at the top of our mast were on, and they were. So we comforted ourselves. We assumed the vessel off our beam had seen us on their ship's radar, or on the watch. But since they weren't doing anything about it, we then assumed they were asleep, drunk, or too busy playing Game Boy.

I opened the hatch and called into the darkness for the skipper. But he was tired and not his old bouncy self. 'Fuck off,' is how he put it.

'What did he say?' asked Chris when I slammed the hatch to.

'He thinks we are more than capable of making this, ah, decision for ourselves.'

'What do you think?'

'I think they're going to hit us.'

'Get him up, I want to go about.'

I slid open the hatch and shouted for the boss again. He stumbled from his bunk. His big head out the hatch, his eyes screwed into the lenses of the binoculars around his neck he said, 'It's past us! Can't you fucking see that?'

All I could see, when a wave wasn't in the way, was looming lights: two rising and falling glowing orbs in the swirl of shadowy spray and wind, one on top of the other; flanked either side by a beast's eyes, red and green, bearing steadily down on us. I told the boss this and he slammed the hatch to.

'Get it on the radio – ask the skipper,' said Chris, a minute later.

Skippy made the radio call. They were a Dutch trawler dragging nets. They had seen us, they noted our course

39

and speed. The trawler captain said he would make a minor course change.

But as the minutes passed and the vessel drew closer and closer, the trawler seemed to make no perceptible change of course. Instead of the bow pointing directly at the cockpit of our boat it now pointed at our cabin. It rode down on us, the bow rising and falling through the big sea, convincing us that the trawler captain had not done a thing. Chris turned the boat up into the wind. I trimmed the sheets. The trawler steamed past the bows. And the boss had a fit.

The way he shouted, you'd have thought we'd hit the boat. Our seamanship was questioned. But it was coy and embarrassed and didn't want to stand up for itself. Besides, we weren't listening anyway. The mad old bastard went back to his bunk, cursing us.

The rest of that night passed without further incident, and by the time we had handed over the watch at four that morning the wind had dropped down to thirty, thirty-five knots.

Two days later we made Corunna.

It was eleven on a Friday night when we motored past the sea-wall, and it was raining. We were all tired, wet, but happy to have made port. All we had talked about for the last two days was a hot meal and bottles of Rioja.

We moored to a buoy in the harbour, cut loose the dinghy, put it over the side and rowed ashore in the rain, laughing.

We went straight for the yacht club bar, an ugly, box-like concrete building overlooking the port. The boys called home. I met the bartenders, Enrique and Manuel.

They were fine, smiling, liveried gentlemen who told me they could change any currency, including the yen; the bar would remain open for as long as we had need of it; and they had something called bifsteak and patatas fritas and would cook it immediately if we wished. We did. I thanked them.

Soon after the meat had begun to spit on the grill in the back kitchen we started talking with the only other men sitting in the empty bar on that rainy night. There were three of them and they had sailed down from Brittany.

These Bretons had been caught in the same blow as us but they had had a few problems. All yachties reckon they have problems. That, so far as I could make out, was the best part of sailing: going to the bar and lying your head off after one of these rough passages.

'So,' we asked them once we were all set up with the Rioja, 'what happened to you?'

The skipper, a small, scruffy, bleached and tanned man in faded jeans, an old sweater and espadrilles, smiled. Then he tapped the table slowly, with his index finger and thumb. This, we understood after some questioning, was an impression of the mast of his boat during the storm.

'Ah,' said Chris. 'Bunda'd.'

The Frenchman did not understand this word, bunda.

'We had a leak,' I told their skipper. 'Almost sunk, but the skipper is a nautical genius. He got us in safe, after a few life-threatening close calls.'

'Ah,' said the mariner, 'we also. But did you have the fog?'

The fog he was talking about was sitting in a big bank just offshore and he had been shoved straight into it, running downwind, at full speed, ahead of this big storm. This wouldn't have been at all impressive if this fog of his hadn't hidden a dangerous coast and his port, and all he had had to navigate with was a sextant, which needs the sun.

'So why not turn into the storm if it was that bad?' I asked him. 'Mast fall off?'

'No,' he said. 'We are all in a small catamaran. The sea was much too big for us.'

41

A catamaran is easier to capsize than we hoped to be after we were through for the night. This was a winning point.

'So – how did you manage to find a port, in the fog, in the middle of a storm, without navigation equipment, if things were really as bad as you said?' I asked him.

'Dolphins,' he replied simply.

This man was a fine liar. A world-class master of the sailing story.

'Dolphins?'

'Exactly.'

We all smiled, nodded and winked. But this Frenchman wasn't rattled. He had communed with nature, a school of the little critters had suddenly appeared at the time of his great crisis and led him off to the mouth of the invisible safe harbour; past the rocks, reefs, and past probably a few whirlpools if we knew what those words were in French. And that was the truth.

Next, he told us that he and his friends were off to cross the Atlantic, via Madeira, to make a delivery to the boat's owner in Martinique (in a boat without navigation equipment, radio, or a mast by the sound of things).

'Nutters,' said Tobin. The food came soon after.

Next day the weather changed and when we were woken by the early sounds of the port and the front nearby, the sun was out and it was hot.

I got up and dressed. I was ready for the front and the bars. A nice, friendly señorita to impress, I was just thinking. A holiday.

'Not today,' said the boss sitting up in his bunk and rubbing a weary eye. 'There are certain things I want done before we do *anything* else!'

'Like what?'

'All the sails must be hosed down, re-folded, and put back in their right bags,' he said.

42

'Is that so?'

'It is.'

'And what else?'

'Well, let me see. Hmm. Ah, yes. The lockers have to be re-packed. Then stuff has got to be taken off to the laundry and after that's done . . .'

'All right. So what will you be doing?' I asked.

'I have to go into town on important business.'

So once he had slipped his tether, changed into his business shorts, and was safely striding out of view, Tobin, Chris and I hoisted our sails, said bye bye to the chores, and skipped up the gang-plank for the morning to visit the Frenchman. On the cut, we told sailing stories touched with raw genius.

Ten very pleasant days passed. With a hole in the hull diagnosed and filled by Moe, Curly, and Larry at the shipyard, the guts swilling with cheap Rioja, and the skin browned by long days out on deck working in the hot sun, we were ready for the next leg down the Spanish and Portuguese coasts. With a storm down our necks we were feeling happy and confident as we slipped the mooring with the tide and motored out past the sea-walls and the old fort into the glittering sea.

'Nice being back at sea,' said the skipper as we chomped on chorizo sandwiches. Next day we got whacked by another storm.

A week and a half later, we floated into Las Palmas on the Canary Islands. The skipper had cooked once. This was a remarkable achievement. There was a cooking rota that implied we would take it in turns to cook every four days.

'Ah, but I'm the skipper,' he would say.

'But you're fat,' said Tobin.

'Exactly. That's why I'm not cooking.'

It had taken us almost a month to get there but by now,

43

having spent all this time together, we were a complement of sorts: the boss and I argued, Chris smothered the flak, Tobin bragged.

The voyage, however, was not treating the boss too kindly. The leak, missing his girl, me – it was all making him a little glum and distant. Finding himself, the mystique of the self, the real he, was no easy chore. 'Sometimes,' he would say, with his big face in the booze after another day working on the boat, 'I wish we'd never gone.'

Not us. We had a fine time and got in trouble as often as possible. Girls to chase were plentiful. Some spoke English. Chris got picked up by a transvestite. Tobin started a food fight in a small restaurant and was chased by police. The holiday spirit was with us and there was an army of the same to play with; over a hundred yachts from all over the world had gathered in Las Palmas for a race the boss had entered us in. Across the Atlantic.

So the week passed, we made friends with other boat-crews, spent long nights telling inflated sailing stories in the Mississippi Steamboat bar moored in the port, and late in the week contemplated taking on a new hand for the Atlantic. To get more sleep at night.

'No males,' said Tobin. 'Blondes – that's what this boat needs.'

'But what if it should upset the balance,' said the boss, trying to sound sensible and sober for a change. 'Right now we work well together. What if we should get someone that didn't fit in?'

'A blonde would fit in nicely,' said Tobin. 'No worries.'

And the day before the race, the answer to Tobin's request appeared on the dock, looking for a passage to Barbados. She was beautiful. A blonde called Molly with impeccable sailing credentials (a typed résumé of experience with letters of reference from skippers of famous Maxi racing boats of the Caribbean), courted by the owners of two of the biggest, prettiest yachts moored in port, both in the race to Barbados. Yet even with these invitations the woman said she would like to come with us, on our cramped little vessel, if we would have her. Naturally, we all felt like having her and decided the little minx must be madly in love with us to make such a foolish decision.

'But,' said the boss, 'are we all sure she won't drive a wedge between us?'

'Nonsense,' we said. 'Don't be so daft. It will make a nice change to have a woman aboard for those three long and lonely weeks at sea.'

So on the morning of the race Molly arrived and was led aboard and shown to her quarters in the fo'c'sle. We filled up with supplies from the supermarket in town, filled the water and fuel tanks at the dock and motored out the port in the warm sun to join the fleet out in the bay for the start of the race. There were over a hundred yachts, pleasure boats and military vessels on the water when the gun went.

'The Big A – here we come!' said the skipper as we set off down the coast under full sail.

'My bunk,' Tobin muttered, holding his head. 'Here I come.'

That first night on the Atlantic, south of Gran Canaria, the wind got up. Molly felt sick but the boss did not want to encourage preferential treatment.

'We're all equals on this boat! We must all do a watch,' he said, nobly. So he went below and fetched her. When she came up on deck he hugged her like a proud father and said, 'That's the spirit! That's my girl!' and we watched his fingers linger on her shoulder just a beat or two longer than necessary.

That night, after dinner, lights out, and much polite and chivalrous behaviour and conversation in the cabin, the boat threatened to broach. We had too much wind for the

45

sails. But the boss wanted his kip and did not wish to be disturbed until it was his turn at the wheel. So the watches rotated on and off until finally the boat was out of control all the time, threatening for a knock-down, and the all-hands was given. Skippy got up in a little grump.

'Where's Molly?' he shouted above the roar of the wind.

'Asleep in the fo'c'sle!' we shouted back, holding on to the mast as the boat tried to sling us overboard.

'Why isn't she up? She should be up here, too!'

We shrugged and set to work. The skipper drove the boat up into the wind, the sails flapped noisily, the loose sheets beat the wood decks, the boat lost all its speed, Molly didn't show, the motor was started to give steerage and we noticed something very pleasant. As we worked gathering the canvas as it dropped to the for'deck, barefoot, in shorts, with no shirt, in the middle of the night, in a howling wind, with waves beating the bow and sending forth great spumes of water, it was warm; like tepid bath water. Very pleasant. Not like Biscay.

A half hour later, when the sails were down, gathered, bagged, and new sails were hoisted and trimmed, we went below and towelled dry. There was no sign of the lovely Molly except on the Maxis.

'She should have got up!' said the boss.

'Probably feeling sick.'

'That's no excuse.'

On the morning of the second day, just after breakfast, Molly finally got up. Then Molly came on deck. Then Molly took all her clothes off. To go sunbathe naked on the for'deck.

'Nice having a lady aboard, isn't it?' said the skipper, grinning as we watched her amble up the deck with a towel over her shoulder.

'Very,' we all agreed. 'Good for morale.'

46

'My birthday soon,' said Tobin. 'I don't want her to have any of those.'

'That's *morals*, not morale, pillock,' said the skipper, cuffing him around the ear and giggling.

But the pleasure of having this beauty aboard was short-lived for the boss. Nights became very unpleasant for the old fox, who had arranged the watch rota so that Molly followed him on, every night. Instead of being able to sit there offering gems of nautical wisdom, and blab the great poems of the Romantics to the young damsel – under moonlight, fingers slowly creeping down her smooth-skinned, tanned shoulders – he discovered, after a few days out of Las Palmas, that a regular – and for him, highly irritating – pattern began to emerge.

Not only was the lovely Molly reliably, according to the boss, fifteen minutes late to relieve him at the wheel for the night watch; but she showed with no penitence. She appeared on deck, earphones wrapped around her lovely ears, singing to the tunes of the Beach Boys: 'Bermuda, Bahamas – Ooo, I wanna take you . . .' she sang. No intimate chats for the skippy, at least another twenty minutes tagged onto his watch as he tried to raise her from her beauty sleep. He quickly tired of it, and her.

Worse, this nightly chirping meant Molly did not concentrate her attentions at keeping the ship aligned with the wind. Going downwind, as we did after a couple of days, we had two boomed-out head-sails. If the boat was not kept in the wind's corridor, the wind would sneak behind one of the sails, and fill it inwards (backing it). When it filled back the way it was meant to be there was a bang fit to crack a rig or split a sail, which always woke us snoozing in our salty bunks below. This whoosh! bang! sent the boss scurrying for the hatch with a mouthful of abuse for the oblivious young beauty. What she accomplished every night was something known as sailing by the lee. Thus the skipper's angry cry of, 'Mo-*lee*!' each time it happened.

Night after night this potentially expensive drama was performed, slowly destroying the boss's composure. Each time he'd return to his bunk at the end of a watch muttering darkly about chumming the girl as shark bait. Defenders of her virtue, we tried to soothe the boss during the daytime, and remind the young lovely, when decency permitted, that it was imperative she concentrate her efforts whilst driving at night or the boss might do something we'd all regret.

'Like what?' asked Molly.

'Well, throw you overboard, maybe.'

But it was all said in vain. Whoosh! . . . Bang! Mo-*lee*! Every night, all week long.

The week slowly drifted by and strange new habits of the skippy's began to surface. At sundown, he insisted Albinoni come piping out the ship's speakers while he stood staring meditatively out at the empty horizon. He studied the knot book and practised making nooses. He spent much time down below deck away from us all. He was not, we saw, having much fun.

And to make matters worse, this great sleigh ride the books promised did not show.

Days passed slowly, entries were made in the log, we slipped at an average of four knots through one time zone, then another, the sky was constantly scanned for the tell-tale trade wind cloud-trains; but the wind blew from all over the place until one day it died completely.

We went swimming.

'Not me,' said the boss, pacing the decks. 'Ought to remember what Alice told us.'

Alice was an Australian we met in the Canaries. She was full of sailing stories. The one the skip referred to was of a passage she had made years earlier across the Pacific.

Whilst fishing off the yacht she crewed, they hooked a hammerhead shark. They pulled the beast up to the boat, gaffing it to bits with a gaffing hook, but the shark thrashed free, broke the line, and slithered off. A couple of days later, two hundred miles from where they had caught the shark, they were becalmed and Alice went over the side for a dip. As she was flopping about she had a queer feeling – as if there was something threatening nearby. The feeling was very strong so, on instinct, she decided to swim back to the boat. Just as she was clambering up the diving ladder on the transom, the shark – mad, mutilated, one-eyed, jaws snapping – lunged up from the water and tried to take a chunk out of her rump. He missed, but she never went back in the water again.

'Ah, but that's a sailing story,' I said. 'Don't believe a word of it.'

But he did, and he whistled the tune from the movie *Jaws* as we dived overboard into the clear blue sea.

For the next two windless days and nights the sails and the boom flapped about, irritated by the roll of the ocean, making a miserable racket and destroying the concentration for the battles of backgammon pitched each day in the hot sun. The only thing to move during the day was Molly rolling over to tan her firm buttocks; or us to pitch over the side for a dip. The boss was not part of this. He sought the shade below, wrote letters, grew a beard and played with his engine. Sometimes he threw a pail of sea-water over the decks and scrubbed them. He wasn't at his most communicative.

On the morning of the third day, becalmed, eleven days into the passage, the boss announced we were exactly half-way across and so could celebrate with a ship's party that evening. The sun set late that afternoon, Albinoni pumped out the deck speakers until Tobin slotted in the Beastie Boys, the stars rose, the skipper fixed the cocktails, and the

49

sea was perfectly flat, like a giant dark blue saucer. Hours passed happily as we sat in the cockpit flirting with Molly. Then someone said, 'What's that?'

We watched running lights appear on the horizon. 'Russian spy ship,' said Tobin. (The boss reckoned the seas were crawling with them.)

'Russian sub,' said Christopher.

'Not funny,' said our leader. He went below to fetch the glasses. 'It's a freighter,' he announced.

As time passed, we watched these same lights approach from all points of the compass, then the boss had a bright idea. 'Better take the wheel,' he said. 'I think we're going in circles.'

From then on, the watch system resumed. Inevitably, the talk switched to whales. The year before, during the same race, a yacht had accidentally run over a whale pup, the mother had fetched the bulls and the bulls had attacked the boat and taken off the rudder. The boat's crew were rescued by another yacht on the race and this worried the boss.

'And that's *not* a sailing story,' he said.

Then a funny thing happened. By 1 a.m. only Molly and I were left on deck. I made a nest of the sail-bags and invited her to have a sit. Molly took her clothes off. More fodder for my volume of sailing stories.

The following morning, I was deep in the chocolate. The Spanish booze had me glued to the bunk and no amount of shaking, swearing, or pleading could raise me for my watch at four that morning. This disgusting behaviour deflected any pesky questions about the night's activities. The day was spent in penance, Molly's unsullied virginity and character intact. (By now we had all come to the firm decision that it would be bad for the ship's morale if carnal relations were established with the young maid. Old friendships evaporate fast under the cruel hand of jealousy; etc, etc.)

Later that day the boss said, 'Bad news, I'm afraid. We might run out of water.'

'How can we run out of water at sea?'

The passage was taking longer than expected, he said. The Trade Winds had not arrived. But this had its benefits, too. After three days of being becalmed, we dropped the sails and fired up the motor. It was time to find the wind.

Days later, rationing for all things was now in place and we ate sparsely, badly, and only from a can. The culinary thrill each day was the fresh bread the cook of the day baked. One measly slice a person. The wind picked up and we finally had twenty knots constant from the south-west. The Trade Winds had come. We did a little dance on deck to celebrate.

Late in the afternoon, Tobin pointed. 'What's that?' he asked.

'What?' said the bearded skipper down below, out of the sun. 'Where?' He poked his head out of the hatch.

'Over there. A long dark . . . hump?'

'Submarine,' said Christopher, sitting in his shorts behind the wheel, his shoulders shooting up and down and his cheeks dimpling as he laughed.

'Not funny. It's got a fin, you bastard,' said the skipper, bounding up onto deck. 'Fetch the binoculars!'

Tobin fetched his camera.

'Why didn't you bring the binoculars?' the skipper asked.

'I need a picture for mum and Karen . . .'

'That's not a fish!' the skipper cried, brushing Tobin aside. 'That's a *whale*!'

It was, too. And it was huge. And for no apparent reason it started bearing down at us. Just before it struck the stern, it dived and we saw a long, curving, dark back and tail over twenty foot in length. 'Shit! I knew this would happen,' the skipper muttered. 'He'll sink us. Jesus. Sound the depth seeker! What kind is it?'

51

Nobody knew, but we were soon joined by his friend and together they played around the boat until nightfall, while Tobin and Molly took lots of pictures.

'Let's hope that's the end of them,' said the skipper, gloomily.

But the whales came back that night. In the morning over tea, we sat in the rising sun in the cockpit with the skipper and his whaling manuals.

'They're Minkes or Pilots,' the boss announced. 'It's a good job they're not Blues. If they were Blues we'd really be bunda'd.'

Molly came on deck. Molly was not interested in whale talk. What Molly was interested in was her Body Glove rubber bikini. It was her favourite and she seemed to have lost it somewhere. Had anyone seen it? she wanted to know. No-one had.

'Never mind,' said Molly. 'Don't need it anyway.' She went off to sunbathe for the rest of the morning.

Up to that moment nobody else in the race had radioed sightings of whales on the daily radio network, which was run by a lady named Sheila in the Turks and Caicos Islands (at 1200 GMT all boats, if they wished, radioed their position to the station). The skipper instructed Chris to tell Sheila we had the company of whales, just in case we were rammed and sunk by the beast before getting off a mayday.

Late that day we made an important discovery. Contrary to the theory that the beast was here to sink us and drive us to the deep, we learnt that the old sop had developed a fierce crush on the boat. In the whaling almanac the skipper had under his pillow, it said that the act of a whale breaking out of the water to stand up on its tail and then crash down on its back was one of the last stages in the courting ritual of the Minke – a whale's way of proposing. And as the other whale had not appeared for almost twenty-four hours, it could only be the little yacht that was

52

the object of his lust and affection. All afternoon long we watched this poor misinformed mammal come leaping out the Atlantic, love-struck, to fall down on his back with a mighty splash.

'What he needs,' said Tobin, 'is a pair of Christopher's glasses.'

'I wish he'd just leave us alone,' said the boss.

The following morning, after another night with the whale, we sighted a sail on the shimmering horizon.

'Get him on the radio,' the skipper barked. 'See if he knows anything about whales.'

The boat was not a member of the fleet. It was an Australian couple on their way to Antigua.

'Got a joke for you,' said Christopher opening conversation. 'Three missionaries are captured in the jungle by a bunch of cannibals . . .'

The Australian parried with another joke, then asked about our route. Chris told him: Barbados, Panama Canal, Galapagos, Marquesas, Darwin, the Indian Ocean, Suez, the Mediterranean, and then home.

'Ah,' said the Australian. 'The milk run . . .'

The Australians, a man and his wife, had been at sea seven years and travelled to every nook and cranny on the planet. At present they were busy pickling a 35-pound dorado they had caught just before tea, the night before. They told us the secret of their fishing and would have told us more, but the boss was impatient for information about whales.

'See if he knows how to get *rid of 'em*,' said the boss, loitering, over Chris's shoulder.

Chris told the man we had company. The man asked how big. 'Twenty to thirty feet,' said Christopher.

'That's nothing, mate. You wait until they're bigger than the boat – *then* you'll have something to worry about. The

Blue Whale in the Pacific – now he's what I'd call a whale!
A *fifty fuckin' footer*!'

'Show off,' said the skipper.

Later that afternoon the whale left us. A few days later,
on December 14, twenty days out of the Canary Islands,
unsunk by leak or whale, we heard, on the ship's radio,
reggae Christmas carols. We were 90 miles off the coast of
Barbados. As luck would have it, it was Friday. Tobin was
the first to spot land. This was a minor irritation to the
boss who had been eagerly calculating land-fall for about
twenty days now.

At 9 p.m. that night, after reaching along the twinkling
lights of the dark coast, on the lee side of a reef, we motored
round the head into Shallow Draft, the port at Bridgetown,
Barbados. There were lots of yachts already moored, some
with lit cabins, forming two sides of a sea-corridor. We
slowly motored towards the quay, putting out the fender
buoys and making ready the warps, and the yachts klax-
oned us as we passed, welcoming us in.

We moored alongside three other boats that had arrived
earlier in the day. It was night, but the quay was bright
with fairy lights and noisy with a calypso band.

'Well, we made it,' said the skipper.

We congratulated him. Then we got drunk and told
sailing stories to anyone who would listen.

The following day we learnt how we did. The skipper
told the committee we motored for x many hours and they
told him we did terribly.

'Don't you worry, skipper,' said Tobin. 'We'll give you
something to be proud of.'

'That's what I'm worried about.'

After three months together we were good at making
trouble. There was a galley moored opposite us in the
harbour that woke us early each morning with loud
calypso. They flew an eight foot by ten foot Jolly Roger.

We stole it. A South African boat moored two boats away, with whom we had nearly fought over a mooring buoy on arrival, had it coming to them, so we stole their dinghy tender and moored it to the Italian boat across the way who also had it coming to them. Tobin organized balcony-jumping competitions into the shallow end of a swimming pool at a nearby bar and almost crippled the young South African skipper. Chris had so much to drink his kidneys hurt and he had to stay in his bunk for two days. And the skipper followed our progress from a distance, mingling with the other owners and skippers, quietly proud that his boat was fast getting the reputation for something.

We were 3000-and-something miles from the know-it-all in the bar back in England. He turned up a few days after Christmas.

'Ah,' he said, striding through the bar area set up on the dock. 'So you made it, eh? Jolly good show. Let me buy you all a drink and tell you about the old Pacific. Now your Pacific . . . Hi! Where are you going?'

The beach.

We stayed another week in Barbados and after Christmas sailed to spend New Year on the other islands. We went to Saint Lucia, and finally to Martinique where the boat came out into dry dock in a beautiful old yard, full of coconut trees and mongrel dogs, to see if the leak could be plugged – it had leaked all the way across.

We had company across the dirt yard. In a shed with a corrugated iron roof, raised up on stilts, was the cat from Corunna with the bouncing mast. The mast lay beside the boat. So they too had made it across, which now was not such a great surprise after seeing the twenty-something footer that an Englishman had sailed across, single-handed, in the race. The little French skipper had gone back to Brittany. The owner was busy painting it, getting it ready for charter work.

It was time for me to leave. I was flat broke again and owed everyone money. After three months of living and laughing and working and playing with these fine men, it broke my heart to say goodbye, but nothing had come up to keep me in the Caribbean so I had to head home, to New York.

'What are you going to do now?' the boss asked me as he, Chris and Tobin stood at the airport to see me off. It was hot and fine. It was winter back in New York and snowing, according to the papers.

'Get a job.'

The flight was called, final boarding.

'Say, skipper, one last thing,' I said.

'What?'

'Lend me a couple of bucks to get home from the airport.'

'Bugger off.' But then he reached into his pocket and pulled out some money and gave it to me. 'Look after yourself,' he said. I kissed the old bastard and headed off for the plane waiting on the hot tarmac.

Over the next couple of years I got letters from the boys with far-away post marks from islands in the South Pacific, the Indian Ocean and the Mediterranean. Tobin ended up in Sydney behind a bar and is expecting a child soon with Sam, a young girl he met in Sydney. Chris had to fly back to England from Australia, broke and sore in the kidneys. But the skipper met his future bride in Sri Lanka. He sailed back to England, two-and-a-half years after leaving, a changed and happy man, so he says. Now he's trying to make enough money to go off and do it all over again.

Three

When I got back to New York I found out Carla was pregnant. She had had an affair with some night-club owner in Miami and was moving down there to set up home. I was almost happy for her. I took her to the bus the day she left. We never talked about it.

I got a job writing a few things for a friend's magazine; but the job wasn't going to turn permanent and I could never get paid when I needed money. Then one night in early February, the phone rang.

'Hey, bum,' said an old, friendly voice. 'Welcome home. When did you get in?'

'About a month ago.'

'Yeah? How was it?'

'Best time of my life.'

'No shit. So how ya doin' for money?'

'Not good.'

'I thought so. So how'd'ya like to make some money?'

It was Sal, a fellow pizza-thrower and man of the coffee mugs and bus trays from the Pizza Palace Restaurant Co., on Amsterdam.

'Sal,' I said, 'right now, I'm so hungry I would consider a long career in sanitation.'

'Well,' Sal said, 'sanitation pays better than this. What we're doing is moving. Are you in?'

'Absolutely.'

'Good.'

Sal told me that the office for this company – Bethlehem Moving & Storage Company – was on the top floor of the building he lived in, over on 8th Avenue. A despatcher from Bethlehem, a shifty-eyed hustler in Sal's opinion, had met Sal on the stairs one afternoon and asked him whether he wanted to make a lot of money and Sal, being a poor bastard like me, said he did. So then Sal was asked if he had any friends who were good workers who also wanted to make a lot of money; that's what made Sal think of me.

I asked him how much we could expect for this work and Sal said, 'Two hundred. Two hundred big ones.'

This was a fat sum. With it I could pay the man in the corner store, order up beer on credit, eat in a diner, and buy boxes of *Tender Vittles Chicken Dinner* for pussy. Fine news indeed.

'We work tomorrow,' said Sal. 'So get an early night, buddy. You're going to need all your strength.'

At the street corner of 27th and 8th at 5:30 on that dark, cold Sunday morning in February I sluiced into view and had to hove up against a lamp-post for support. The night had finished about ten minutes earlier. It had been quite a fiasco. Belly dancers, booze, a whole slew of already for-gotten faces. I had been on the town with my pal, Ramin.

A squad of moving men were milling around three beaten-up Mack Bobtails. They sipped coffee and smoked. They looked strong, healthy and well-rested, in army fatigues, money belts and work boots. This was a shocking contrast to my condition.

On one of the trucks I read, with great difficulty: *BETHLEHEM MOVING & STORAGE COMPANY Where the customer always comes first! Local and Long Distance – our speciality!*

And it was written on a truck that didn't look like it could make it across the State line.

So I was up against this post, generally overwhelmed,

sweating, even though the temperature was minus five, when a man with a clipboard, a bright red bandana, curly black hair, strong Levantine features, jeans and work boots came over to ask who I was. I told him I was a friend of Sal's.

The man introduced himself: 'Eli – Foreman.' And took my hand and almost broke it. This made me feel very sick. But he was friendly, this man. He told me how happy he was that I had come to work with them at Bethlehem, and what a fine day we'd spend working together.

'Yeah.'

A young man in a bandana and shades had started to pump out push-ups. He was doing them whilst smoking, on the cold pavement, at 5:30 on a Sunday morning.

'So,' said Eli Foreman. 'You like work, Saama?'

'That's right,' I said.

'Good. We have a long day. I hope you are feeling strong, Saama.'

A young man slouched out the open window of one of the trucks. Eli started talking to him. To my tender hearing it sounded like a squadron of F-15's going to after-burner somewhere near the larynx. As I turned to walk away I bumped into something with a weight belt and big boots.

'What the fuck happened to you, buddy?'

'Sal!'

'Have a good night?'

'I'm not sure, yet.'

'You get a little bent outa shape there, pal?'

'Perhaps.'

Eli Foreman joined us with the man who had been slouched in the truck window.

'This is my good friend, Alon,' Eli said. 'He will be foreman for you. He is really good man. You work with him, Saama.'

We shook and this fellow nearly broke my hand, too.

59

Like all the other men he was strong and fit-looking with olive skin and black curly hair. He smoked a cheroot and had a small gold lion hanging from his left ear. Without a word he beckoned for me and Sal to follow. The moment had arrived. Retribution.

Forty-five minutes later I was ready to run for my mattress. This moving was very hard work and we hadn't even started. All we had done so far was re-pack the moving supplies on the trucks. Yet my fellow movers had barely broken a bead and I was pouring it off, about 10W40 grade, distilled.

I stood off to one side and rubbed my sore head. One of the boys said, 'Eighteen hours or more, Saama! If we have luck it will be very good day!'

Nuts to you, my friend, I thought.

Not long after, a crew of about twenty men climbed up into the cabs of this fleet of battered trucks and we rumbled up 8th Avenue. It was still dark, I think, and the streets empty. If my eyes were translating properly. We were going uptown.

'Saama,' one of the men said to me as we rode, 'why you do the moving? Is really. . .is really *ga'bidge* this job.'

'Two hundred bucks,' I replied. 'Not the sort of money you laugh at.'

But they did. These boys howled. In fact they made such a noise it should have made me worry, but I was not capable of much mental agility at that time.

Fifteen minutes later we pulled up outside the freight entrance of a thirty-storey building on 48th Street. The customers were waiting for us when we jumped down from the cabs: two soft-bellied, pasty-white, fur-wearing, balding middle-aged fashion executives who looked mad about something.

'You're late!' one said.

60

'You said you'd be here at six-thirty! We've been wait-ing!' said the other, looking at his gold Rolex.

'Flat tyre,' Eli Foreman said, walking off. The customers followed, arms crossed, shaking their heads and whispering in conference about something. We unloaded the supplies.

Shortly afterwards we were led to the service elevator wheeling two towers of dollies; four great rolls of bubble wrap, and a mountain of different-sized cardboard packing boxes. We were taken up to the thirteenth floor to look at the work.

A month, by my estimation: a factory floor of slewing machines, desks, cupboards, computer terminals, shelf-units, and the contents of eight run-down offices.

'Be finished by seven – sum'sing like zis,' said Eli Foreman. 'But you know – I muss talk wiz you first. We have to make agreement about tip. For biz'niss.'

'What?' said the customer.

'*Teshe*,' said Eli. 'Usual for customah to tip ten, fifteen pa'cent of job. *Is usual!*'

'Hey! Nobody said nothin' about this to *me*!' said the customer.

Nobody would. The *teshe*, or tip, was a piece of business that took place between the foreman of the job and the customer, not the office of Bethlehem and the customer. I had heard all about it in the truck. The boys got very excited talking about it. Teshe was how the moving man made the money to take him to Rio; and Rio was quite the hot spot for these young men. And they were all young Israeli men, except me and Sal. Once National Service cut them loose, they took the first plane out of Tel Aviv and made straight for New York City where they worked for other Israelis in the moving trade, lived seven to a room in places like Flatbush, Brooklyn and saved money. Since their bosses ripped them off with wages, they had to make money on the *teshe*. The amount of the *teshe* was determined by the foreman's skill at putting the squeeze on the customer. Eli Foreman was an ace, so the boys said. The boys fought to get on his crew. And this was what this was all about: money. So all the crew stood around, listening and smoking, as this negotiation took place, refusing to lift a hand until it had been settled.

'Is usual!' Eli insisted, outraged and indignant. 'Everybody *muss make tip*!'

Heads nodded, arms crossed and faces scowled. I sat on a dolly and sweated.

But Eli was an old pro. He unzipped his money belt and pulled out the contracts for the job. Then he beckoned for the man to go with him to a place in private for a discussion and signature.

'Please sir,' he said. 'You muss not worry. We make good business. Is no problem. Come.'

Eli grinned at us before taking the customer off and we set to work. Blankets, dollies, packing boxes and boxes of packing tape were given to me. I didn't know what to do with them. I gave them to someone else. Then I pushed a couple of dollies when they were loaded. But these things don't have brakes. They have four wheels which set themselves in a random pattern, normally the opposite direction from wherever you chose, leaving you face down on the carpet looking quite the fool.

'Try packing, Saama,' Alon said, watching me struggle.

After a couple of minutes packing I was ready to try something else. The things they expect you to do with filing cabinets, chairs, desks, dummies and computer terminals require the arms of an octopus and the patience of a saint.

'Saama,' Alon said not long after. 'You pack like shit. You carry computer.'

So that was all I did all morning, carry computer. When it was time for lunch, we sat down in the freight hall and had pizza and coke. An old bum tried to rustle some work, pushing the dollies up the ramps to the trucks, but one of the foremen shooed him away. Alon said, 'Your friend, Sal – he no like the work, Saama.'

Sal was not cut out for manual labour. He spent all morning running out to buy coffee and cokes when he felt like it. He was the only one doing this. They were not impressed with Sal. Soon after lunch was finished Eli Foreman came round to tell us we were working too fast, we should slow down, use ten times more packing tape and materials, and generally behave in a more businesslike manner (movers charge by the hour; the foreman gets a cut of all business). Ten hours later we were behaving so businesslike they told us to get up from our seats and speed up. By midnight we were done. We huddled around the trucks dog-tired and sore. We were down on 22nd and Lex.

Eighteen hours of manual labour is rough. But the money – kitty food, a ticket to Rio, cigarettes, coffee, beer – this was why I went to work. These simple pleasures.

'For you, my friend,' said Eli Foreman, giving me an envelope.

I thanked him and ripped it open, but there weren't many bills inside. Only two, in fact. A twenty and a five. I counted again, slow, just in case I was so tired I was hallucinating and there was a hundred tucked in there somewhere. There wasn't. Twenty-five crummy dollars, not a cent more. I was promised a minimum of two hundred for this job. I reminded my friend Eli.

Eli shook his head and tsk-tsked. 'Is really big muthah-fuckah this guy! 'E no honest. Tell me sum'sing this morning. Tell me sum'sing now. Is different. *Teshe* no good!'

No good? At this rate my fee for the day weighed in around a buck and a nickel an hour, maybe a little less. And that's if old Eli was telling me the truth and not pocketing the money himself. For eighteen hours of work, under stressful circumstance, this revelation was enough to warrant a little temper or two.

'My friend,' Eli said smiling and putting a hand on my shoulder. 'Calm down. Is no problem. You muss come to th'office tomorrow – sum'sing like zat. We have cheque for you. Don' worry!'

So I left to go home, ate in a diner, bought a box of cat food and a beer and fell straight to sleep that night.

9 a.m. the following morning I hammered on the unmarked bell of Bethlehem Moving & Storage Company's premises. No-one answered. I rang again. This time a voice from the intercom said something like, 'Qen?'

I explained who I was and my position.

'Ah. One minute.'

I waited one minute. I waited five minutes. I had the feeling that whoever this bastard was he would have kept me waiting thirty-five minutes if I had not stuck my finger to the buzzer and kept it there. The intercom burst into life. I couldn't understand a word of it but whoever it was must have got fed up with my ringing because the door opened. I zoomed up three flights of stairs.

A short man, smoking, wearing nothing but a set of black Jockey Y-fronts, was waiting at the top of the stairs. 'What you want?' he demanded.

'Money,' I said.

'No cheques today! Come back Thursday!'

I wanted my money. We had an argument. I lost. He said the accountant dealt with that side of the business. The accountant came in Thursdays. 'Call Thursday,' he said. 'We see what we can do.' Then he slammed the door in my face.

That was my first meeting with Izic. For the next six weeks I worked for the man without being paid a nickel. Each time I asked for my money he had some excuse, some

64

promise, but no money. I had to borrow from the newsman and got deep into debt; but this was the only work I'd heard about, so I kept at it. Then, one afternoon, I got whiff of a scheme to fix him.

I was up in his office at the time, and as usual Izic was bragging. The future was bright and prosperous for Bethlehem, he informed me. But it lay in the long distance. And for the long distance he needed someone special. Somebody not like all the others who worked for him. Somebody with the *rare talents*!

So I asked what exactly he meant by a man with these rare talents. He looked up and said, 'Someone who can speak the fluent English! Someone I can *trust* with truck!'

A truck, even the crummy crates he had in his fleet, is worth a lot of money. In Mexico I'd heard you got great money for anything with four wheels that could run further than a block. Without a moment's hesitation I said, 'Then look no further, boss. I am that man.'

Old Izic was not so sure about the idea. I wasn't Israeli. But I was legal. This was invaluable in the cross-country trucking business with men being lifted off the truck and thrown into deportation camps down at El Paso because they didn't have work papers. I could save Bethlehem a lot of money. Izic called me his friend. Then he clapped me on the back and said he'd think about it.

A few days later he appointed me number one cross-country trucker. So now I had a new elevated position in the company, long-distance truck driver, which was a gig all the boys wanted: to be paid to see America. Not that I planned on seeing America; I planned on seeing Mexico. But a promotion meant I did not have to do moves around town, which I hated anyway. The only glitch in the scheme, as far as I could see, was Alon. Izic wanted him to ride with me because Izic trusted him. But I had 3000 miles to make a case to Alon for a trip south of the border, so

I worked, and waited, and finally, at 3 a.m one Thursday at the end of March, we stood in Izic's office ready to embark.

'So lees'en,' Izic said, stubbing out one cigarette and lighting another, 'you muss be Lincollen, Caleyfornia, Monday, eigh'-thirty. No later. Customer waiting.'

'But Izic,' Alon said, 'when we sleep?'

This troubled me, too. We had just completed three nineteen-hour days loading – a normal day's work in the moving business; there was no bed in the truck, not enough legroom with the bags we had to make a roach comfortable, and now he wanted us to set off immediately and drive all the way to Lincoln, California, without stopping anywhere to sleep. This did not bother the boss.

'*Whaa*!?' he shouted angrily. 'You have plenty time for sleep! I give you three hours a day for the rest! You make good sleep in three hours!'

This three hours he was talking about did not account for fuelling or eating.

'My frendz,' he said, 'this job berry important for Bethlehem. I know you muss make some sleep. But, in any event – I need truck back here Friday! Or I lose *big* commer-shall!'

Friday. That was eight days to go across, unload in North California, unload in Los Angeles, load in Los Angeles, load in San Francisco and drive home. Alon tried arguing sanity and safety with him. Izic got mad. Alon reminded him we weren't in the Israeli Army. Izic threw a wobbler. So that's how we left it. You can't reason with a lunatic. We were to call him every day to tell him where we were.

'And one more t'ing!' Izic barked as we started for the door. 'Truck muss have service!'

Alon asked him where we should find a shop to get this truck service.

66

'*Tsk*! Is no problem! Truck-stop!' Izic said.

This would add time. They argued in Hebrew. Alon lost. Izic gave Alon an envelope of cash containing $1000 fuel, toll and fine money – he didn't trust me with a nickel – and finally it was time to leave. But Izic was too smart to have us walk out of his office mad, so he smiled, then wrapped our hands in his and looked us straight in the eye. 'Good luck, my frendz,' he said. 'But be quick, customer waiting.'

Our truck, an old Mercedes Bobtail, was parked on the corner of 29th and 8th. The heap had a cracked wind-screen; large sticker marks on the windshield from the DOT for illegal parking violations; mirrors that were taped in place and held to the door with string; graffiti over the big boxy body; a bumper that was bent and hanging by the bald front tyre; no fire extinguisher; no hazard triangle; no first aid kit; a speedo that didn't work; a clutch that sounded like a pinball machine on full tilt. It was an average New York City truck. It belonged on the streets of Manhattan, but take it to the country where they have things like laws and this crate was an infraction infection.

I mentioned Mexico to Alon.

'This is dishonest, Saama. What you thinkin' 'bout?'

Combined, Izic owed us near three grand. Alon still trusted him to pay. Not me. I had the firm impression Izic was a bird ready to fly the coop. He couldn't pay his staff, couldn't pay his bills, avoided all telephone calls and only answered the phone under the pseudonym of John. Even now, the end of the month, when everybody moved, when the board above Eddy's desk should have been littered with job slips, there was no business. Izic kept himself from being lynched by telling his illegal workers he was expecting large sums of money from a mysterious Israeli investor, but he had been saying this for some time. Tempers were

67

running high. We had the truck. I reminded Alon of all of this. Alon was not interested.

'Saama,' he said, 'we go to Caleyfornia, *not* Mexico.'

'We'll see about that.'

We put our bags in the cab and fired up the old diesel. On 10th Avenue at 44th, we bought 70 gallons of fuel and coffee. Then Alon asked me an interesting question: 'Saama,' he said, 'you want to drive?'

This was of interest only because I didn't know how to drive a big truck. Neither Izic nor Alon knew this. If Izic was going to lie to me I would do the same without qualm. And since the Department of Motor Vehicles allows any fool with a regular licence to operate a truck up to a weight of 25,000 pounds, I was legal. But this Bobtail was thirty feet long, over ten feet wide, did not have an overhead rear-view mirror, nor an automatic transmission, and the brute demanded the co-ordination of a church organist on the pedals to double the clutch. Without this act you can't get out of first gear. First gear to LA would be six hundred hours of driving. It's important to get out of first gear.

'Best thing is for me to read the map,' I said.

'You be DJ,' Alon said.

So we listened to one of Alon's fifteen Doors tapes for a while and then I tried to sleep. To do this there were two choices: upright with the head smacking against the glass, or lying down with the head smacking against the gear-shift. Helmets were not supplied with this truck. The trick to lying down was a variation on the rock-climber's three-point brace: forehead against the shift stick, knee firm against the dash, one foot hard to the roof. In theory, with this accomplished you could sleep through six barrel rolls or its equivalent of a hundred miles down I.80. This was about as comfortable as it got. I napped until Alon woke me near eight the following morning.

'Pennsylvania, Saama,' Alon said, yawning. 'Is really beautiful, uh?'

I saw we were parked on the hard shoulder of a four-lane blacktop and it was flinging down rain. Outside was farm country; bullet silos, barns and fields of grass. I rubbed my eyes and opened the window.

'But Saama,' Alon said, 'we have problem. Som'sing wrong wiz 'er. Go faster than forty . . .' Alon shook his head. 'Is really no good! Izic motherfucker put too much weight in truck. She make this . . .' and he showed me the motion of a snake. 'Sometimes with big wind really . . .' and he showed me the sort of gesture to indicate this snake could go shooting off the highway taking with it half the road users of Pennsylvania. 'Really no pro-feshanal,' he said, laughing.

Professionalism was the running joke at Bethlehem. When things were dropped, broken, or tossed out the back of a truck in some fit, a wit always shouted, 'Pro-feshanal!' Or, 'An-shurance!' When wrong addresses were given by the despatcher, or a truck arrived at a job without packing materials the boys shouted, 'Pro-feshanal!' Because it wasn't. This was the key. When the boss told you he had no money, he probably did. If he called you, 'My friend!' he was about to ask you to do a night job up in the South Bronx, a midnight pick-up. And if he gave you the address of a client, the thing to do was toss it in the bin and call the client yourself. Nothing was ever correct at Bethlehem Moving & Storage Company. Even the business cards we proudly gave out to the poor doomed customers were misspelt. And now, as we sat looking out the muddy windscreen, dopey with tiredness, I noted the right blade didn't work and the left blade made what looked like a kid's finger-painting on the screen. Somewhere out ahead was the road. Somewhere to the left of us, I estimated.

'Bethlehem ga'bidge!' Alon offered.

69

We jumped down from the cab into the rain and cleaned the glass. As we worked, Alon said to me, 'I berry tired, Saama. Berry tired. But, if no for Izic – we no see America!'

This was not the sort of line I wanted old Alon to take. Not if we were to head south of the border. Still, things were looking promising. We weren't two hundred miles out of New York, and the truck was weaving. Without doubt things would get much worse.

With the glass wiped I wasted a lot of time helping Alon get comfy. After, I adjusted the mirrors, then the seat height and position, then I studied the shift pattern and passed at least ten minutes fiddling with the Walkman, the switches by the wheel, and the tapes. I wanted to be sure Alon was deep in sleep.

With nothing left to fiddle with, I released the air brakes, pushed the heavy clutch twice and tried to engage a gear. I couldn't. I pumped the clutch three times, four times, missed the gear, got irritated, floored the clutch then took two hands to the stick and muscled first into the slot, then stomped on the gas. The truck hopped forward like a fourteen-ton kangaroo. Not a squeak came from Alon.

Now, hauling along at the vast rate of 4 m.p.h., I went for second. The truck slewed from one empty lane to another (steering being sensitive with no hands on the wheel). Second was successfully engaged.

'Pro-feshanal, Saama,' muttered Alon.

Over the next couple of hours I played with my new toy. The brakes worked but hitting them was like taking a ride at *Space Mountain*: the truck dived and pulled hard to the right. Naturally the indicators did not work, nor the hazards, and at anything over forty the truck acted like it had been drinking.

But I learnt something: truckers flash twice when another truck is safely past to indicate the passing truck can pull in front. The passing trucker then turns on all the running lights once, in thanks, the near equivalent of the *Emily Post Book for Road Etiquette*.

That afternoon we tried to get a service. As usual Izic was wrong. Truck-stops service trucks twenty-four hours a day – if they're American, and made with Imperial parts. For $99.99 you can get an oil, lube and filter job. But the Mercedes was put together with metric parts. Each time we came to a truck-stop the man at the shop said the same thing. 'No oil filters for Mercedes.' After we had tried three stops Alon turned to me and said, 'He is really fuckin' asshole, Izic,' which was just what I needed to hear. So I asked him if he had brought his passport.

'Saama, what you thinkin'?'

'Oh, you know. A little cocktail. A holiday. . .'

'No,' said Alon.

Just after two that afternoon we came to a large billboard on I.80. It said, *DIAMOND JAY'S TRUCK STOP 2 Miles*. We took the exit ramp off the highway and rode up a winding two-lane, with semis passing us from the opposite way. We went to the truck shop and parked alongside a shiny Peterbilt and trailer with twin chrome stacks, enough lights to decorate the Christmas tree at the Rockefeller centre, and a custom-painted walk-in sleeping cabin at the rear of the tractor that had us both eyeing it with sore-eyed jealousy. All trucks on the highway had sleeping berths in the rear. All of them except ours, of course.

When we jumped down from the cab the trucker was standing there, smoking. He was a cowboy with pointy boots and a big gut. He asked us where we were headed. We told him we were going across to California, San Francisco and Los Angeles.

The trucker thought this was one of the funniest things he had heard in a long time, considering how the truck sounded, which was sick. But I didn't care. If the thing

71

never started again I didn't mind, provided someone could be persuaded to buy it from me.

So we left this trucker laughing on the macadam and went inside the shop to find a mechanic. The shop was the size of an aircraft hangar. Two rigs, over a long pit, were being worked on. In an office nearby, a radio played country music. We followed the noise of a hydraulic gun to the front of a Freightliner. A man came out the pit. I asked him if he could service a Mercedes.

'*Mer*-cedes!' he snorted. 'Is that overseas?'

'German.'

'Don't think we have the parts,' the man said, lighting a cigarette. Alon cursed. This was good news. I was half-tempted to ask if he wanted to buy it, but before I could say a word the mechanic said he would make some calls, if we would wait.

Minutes later he announced he could do it, though it would take a couple of hours, because he was backed up at present.

We went to test the facilities. A truck-stop has great facilities for kids. We played video games; ate hamburgers, apple pie and ice cream; browsed in the truck store; bought T-shirts with pictures of eagles and the name of the truck-stop printed below; purchased sportsman's caps with *American by birth, Southern by the Grace of God* on them; watched TV in the Driver's Lounge; played more video games; and when the truck was ready we decided we had to call Izic and check in. It was now late Friday afternoon.

'Where are you, Saama?' he asked gruffly. I told him. There was a pause. I knew exactly what he was doing. He was looking up at the road chart of America above his desk to pinpoint our position.

'Saama,' he said. 'Why you no in Chicago?'

Chicago was ten hours down the road. I would have liked to have been in Chicago. If I had been in Chicago I

72

would have been in bed in Chicago sleeping the way normal people do after so many hours of work, not running around the countryside looking to get a service for a German truck that no one could service. I explained the problem with the parts and the weave. Izic didn't give two shakes about either. 'I not happy wid you!' he shouted. 'You should have made much better progress.'

'What did he say?' Alon asked when I put the phone down. I told him. 'Is really motherfucker this man!' said Alon.

Near eight that night, on an unlit snowy highway, as we had just crossed the Illinois line, there was the sound of a twin cannon going off and all hell broke loose. The steering went to shit. The truck bucked violently across two lanes of traffic missing every car nearby and Alon woke with a jump. He asked what was going on but I couldn't tell. There was a god-awful racket coming from the rear, I had mush for steering, and fourteen tons of moving truck that made great charges across three lanes of Friday night commuter traffic whenever it felt like it.

However, it was our good fortune I've spent a lot of money on slot cars and video arcades. Getting a car sideways or backwards on the *Rolling Thunder* Video Game is fifty cents lost. No extended play. The thing to remember is not to use the brakes, or the gas, and always, always steer into the skid. We tried this and soon we were pulling up on the hard shoulder.

'Motherfucker Izic!' Alon shouted when we were pulled up. 'He nearly keel us!' Us and maybe thirty others. I set the air-brakes.

'Too much weight in truck! Too much! I tell him this!' Alon shouted. 'Is really fuckin' crazy!'

True, but every bad turn has a good turn as my dear old Granma is fond of saying. And the good turn was Mexico. For sure old Alon would soon be ripe for a run down to the

73

Cerveza Country if things carried on the way they were going.

We jumped down from the cab and went back with a flashlight to find out what part of the truck had gone missing. It was the tyres. Both rear tyres left side were blown. Some rubber shards hung off the rims and the aluminium wheelwell looked like someone had smacked it with a sledge. Ah, and the rims – ruined, possibly beyond repair. This would cost Izic up the wazoo.

'Perfect,' I said. 'Look at 'em! Smashed!'

Alon stared quizzically at me. I explained that now we probably wouldn't have enough money to get everything fixed and this was what I hoped because I'd had enough of the rock climber's three point brace and waking up bolt-rigid each time the truck hit a bump, thinking my friend might have fallen asleep and we were about to have a head-on with a semi. But this didn't worry him. What worried him was being late for the customer.

'You're worrying about the customer?' I asked.

'We really be late now!'

'You're a crazy bastard.'

'But, Saama, is a'venture, no? What happens it happens! You must enjoy! Make some fun!'

We had a little talk about fun. My theory was, the beach, tall chilly ones, and girls was a lot more fun than being involved in a truck wreck. Alon didn't agree.

'Saama,' he said, looking deeply confused, 'you not thinking about the work.'

'No.'

We went back to the cab and settled to wait. There was no chance we were going to walk anywhere. It was sub-zero, pitch black and snowing. Twenty minutes later a trooper pulled up and we jumped down to talk to him.

'Say, are you guys foreign?' he asked.

'New York,' I said.

New York is the answer you give to anyone west of the Hudson River. You can be blind drunk and babbling pidgin Armenian, but as long as you say you are from New York, they accept it.

The trooper nodded. We explained our problem. He said he'd radio a tow truck. Just before we got back in the truck, he had some parting words of advice for us. He said we should not stay in the truck, on no account. We asked him why and he said, 'Just last week not two-hundred yards from here a family was pulled up on the hard shoulder when a rig ploughed in back of 'em. *Wiped the whole bunch out*! Truck driver had fell asleep at the wheel! Yup, I made four hours overtime that night . . .'

His advice was to sit up on the embankment in the snow and freeze to death.

'What happens, happens,' Alon said. 'I don't care.' He climbed back into the cab and I followed.

'Alon,' I said, 'now doesn't Mexico seem like a good idea in light of all this? Truck driving is a dangerous business. The trooper has me convinced we are in mortal . . .'

'Saama, let's not talk about this until we get to Caleyfornia!'

'But think about it. How many men do you know who have been mowed down by a tractor-trailer whilst sitting in a bar?'

He started humming *Riders on the Storm*. I made a pillow up against the snowed glass and decided the next truck-stop we'd have to buy some new tapes.

An hour later there was a bang on the driver's side window. The repair crew had arrived, jacked the truck and fitted new tyres without waking us. They charged us three-hundred-and-fifty dollars. Not enough by my reckoning. Changing tyres on this highway was more dangerous than working for the Israelis. I tried to persuade Alon to give

75

them everything, but three-hundred-and-fifty was all they got.

Eight hours later we blew another set of tyres on the opposite side. This time I was sleeping and Alon was driving. No smash. But this was beginning to get me worried – how long would our luck hold and how often was this going to happen?

'Tell you what,' I said. 'When we get this thing fixed, let's take it into Chicago and sell it.'

'Saama,' Alon said, 'shut up.'

The tyre man did not arrive until seven the following morning. We had strayed off the Interstate onto a minor road during the night. So Alon had to hitch a ride to the truck-stop over on the Interstate to fetch him. But there was a problem: the shop only stocked re-treads. The mechanic's parting words were: 'They may hold to California. Then again, they may not. You boys ought to know within six hundred miles.' Six hundred miles was bang, smack, crash in the middle of the Rockies.

Once we got back on the Interstate we stopped at a 76 truck-stop for breakfast and called Izic.

'How are you, my friend?' Izic asked.

'A little pissed off.'

'Why, Saama?'

I explained what had happened in the last ten hours. When I told him how much money it had cost him ($750), he hit the roof.

'*Saama!*' he yelled. 'This is your fault! You do not check tyres like I tell you! Is impossible this truck overweight! Impossible! I check truck myself!'

I was glad he had said all this because I happened to have a slip of paper from the scales at the truck-stop showing that the weight of our truck was 35,000 pounds – 10,000 over what it was built to carry. It gave me great pleasure to tell him about the weight. All he could say was, 'I see. In any event you must continue.'

'What if we crash?'

'Hold, Saama.' Izic would always put you on hold when he was angry. Minutes later he came back on the line and said, 'Saama, you have come to weigh-station?'

All commercial trucks on the highway have to pull off to run over the scales at weigh-stations. Izic had told me about this at our briefing in New York. Every truck is licensed to carry only so much weight. The stations were there to ensure you don't do what we were doing – running with too much freight. So far none had been open. I told him this. I asked him what he wanted me to do when I came to an open station.

'Pretend you not see it. You understand, Saama?'

I understood perfectly. The bastard wanted me to break the law. But I said all right because running past an open station in a crummy truck with Bethlehem Moving & Storage Company written all over it in funky Hebrew script, in the corn country of the redneck, was bound to get us in trouble. For sure we would both be locked up. But being locked up meant a bed for the night and a little peace from this knucklehead. This was attractive. I asked Izic about bail.

'Tsk!' Izic replied. 'No one put you in the jail!'

'But say they do – are you going to pay to spring us?'

'Of course! I never leave my guys in the shit. But in any event, Saama, you muss hurry. You muss be Lincollen eigh'-thirty Monday morning. Client waits . . .'

The client wasn't the only one. The way things were going he'd have to take second dibs after the Reaper. Anyway, there was another consideration – money. We'd spent tons of it. As Izic hadn't paid us for the last six weeks, we had dipped into the grand to buy our curios. Thus, all we had left was about seventy-five bucks.

77

'Izic,' I said, 'we got a little problem with money.'

'What?'

'We're out of cash. After this tank, we can't go anywhere until you put some money on the wire.'

'*Whaaaa*?' he screamed. 'Why you no money? I give Alon tousand dollar! *Tousand dollar, Saama*! Where it go?'

'Well, on a number of things . . .' Apart from tyres and the service I explained my finances. Food in truck-stops is very expensive. Telephone calls to the office – they cost a lot of money, too. And all truck drivers wear caps. I had to have three. This stuff mounts up. Not to mention the knick-knacks, pins, new tapes (*20 Trucking Originals* featuring Red Sovine and Dave Duddley), T-shirts and whatnot. I told him all this.

Old Izic hit the roof. When Izic hits the roof he sounds much like a man in need of a tracheotomy. All you hear is wheezing as words bottle-neck in the back of his throat. This allows plenty of time to pass the phone to Alon. They spoke. Izic was not happy with me. Nothing unusual there, a symmetry in fact. But Izic agreed to go to Western Union and put another five hundred on the wire for us. But only on one condition.

'What's that?' I asked Alon.

'I muss keep you out of stores, Saama.'

We laughed about that for at least four exits down the highway.

Late that night we passed into Iowa. The highway was not lit, nor were the signs for the weigh-stations. The place was dark and snowy and empty. The lights on the truck were about as good as bicycle lamps. We steered by looking ten feet ahead and to the side at the broken white lines on the empty snow-flecked highway. This was hard on eyes that were already sore and sometimes hallucinating. We stopped at truck-stops, whenever we saw the glow of red and green neon ahead, to wash our faces and buy jumbo

78

cups of coffee. Between the hours of midnight and 2 a.m. I made some calculations: thirty-two ounces of coffee lasts forty to fifty miles at the wheel. Sixty-four ounces of powdered milk for coffee per shift equals two hours of juice, or eighty miles with stops. An ounce therefore would be drunk for every three miles behind the wheel. One thousand man-ounces to California. I worked all this out and it took me about two hours to do it, too. But then I had another thought: this coffee-drinking was bound to make a mess of the intestinal tract and speed up the heartbeat to coronary proportions. Alon needed to know this. I gave him a shake. I told him we needed some rest and healthy analgesics like beer.

'You wake me up to tell me this?' Alon asked.

'It's important we see eye to eye on this.'

'Saama, you crazy.'

We did not see one open weigh-station that night.

'Maybe they close all the way to Caleyfornia,' Alon said just after dawn, when the trucks on the road were still running with all their lights lit.

But around eleven the following morning we were nearing North Platte, halfway through the farm lands of Nebraska on I.80, when there was this sign at the side of the road: WEIGH-STATION . . . ONE MILE . . . OPEN.

Trucks in front started to pull off the highway at the exit ramp for the station. The hut and scales were not more than thirty feet from where we would pass by on the empty Interstate.

'They must see us, uh?' Alon said.

This crate stood out like an eyesore in broad daylight. With the two-hundred-foot-high column of black smoke polluting the local air-space, I would have to say you could almost have seen us coming in Los Angeles. But we had orders. Customer waiting.

A long line of trucks waited to go over the scales as we rumbled past.

About a quarter mile down the road, a brown car with a rack of flashing blue lights appeared in the rear-view mirror. It was a trooper. Alon said, 'Saama, remember – I no work for Bethlehem. I come for ride.'

I pulled over on the hard shoulder and a patrol woman in a brown uniform with a badge, a cowboy hat, and Ray Ban Aviator glasses, came up to the cab. I looked in my mirror. My face was unshaven, my hair was greasy. My eyes were two red pools in a sea of fatigue. My shirt looked like the cat had been sick on it. I had just the right sort of haggard profile to be considered a menace to other road-users. Arrest us, please.

'D'you know you jus' ran past an open weigh-station?' she asked me.

'No, officer,' I said. 'But I have to tell you, this is some of the prettiest country I . . .'

'Just gimme your licence.'

I gave her my licence and she took it back to her car. When she returned she had some questions. Was my name Keith? Did I have a brother named Keith? How tall was I? Was I sure my name was not Keith? I was: my licence mentioned nothing of this Keith.

'Well, you gonna have to go up the road to the next exit, make a turn over the highway, go back down the highway a coupla miles, make another turn, and this time, fella, run that truck over them scales.' And just in case I had other plans, she kept my licence.

A quarter of an hour later we joined the line at the scales. When it was our turn to drive over, we came to a stop on the ramp and a voice on the loud-speaker by the driver's side window said, 'Driver, park your vehicle and bring your documents inside.'

What documents? We had one dog-eared registration

card, an almost illegible stat of the insurance, and my confiscated licence. That was all.

'What else do you think they want to see?' I asked Alon.

'My working papers, Saama!'

We jumped down from the cab into the cold sunlight and walked across the lot towards the concrete hut. A cowboy with polarized glasses came out of the door carrying a fancy document holder under his arm.

'That is really for pro-feshanal, Saama,' Alon said, regarding the holder.

There was a counter and a number of drivers standing at it with document folders open when we walked in. These things, I noted with great satisfaction, were giant credit card holders, packed with coloured cards. We had two scraps of dog-eared paper. Both white.

There were four officers inside. One stood at the counter talking to a driver, three sat at desks in front of a large window. The window looked out at the scales, a verge of grass, and the highway. A rig was up on the scales. On the walls were road safety posters. *Tiredness Kills*! was one of them. This was something to send Izic when we got locked up, I thought. A picture of a jack-knifed rig, on its side, in a ditch, with a car overturned next to it. Plenty of room on that trailer to write *Bethlehem Moving & Storage Company*. The only thing missing from the picture were the number of cars involved. Only two in this picture. We needed about thirty.

A young officer with a crew-cut and a bull neck came to the counter and leant on it heavily. 'Well,' he said with dollops of satisfaction, 'it ain't no surprise you ran past now, is it?'

Of course not. But I couldn't tell him this. 'Why is that, officer?' I asked.

''Cuz you're ten thousand pound over!' the man said.

What followed was sort of predictable enough. He asked

me if I had an ICC card. I asked him what an ICC card was.

'We gotta pair here,' he said.

Then he asked me for a list of things I had never heard of before: Bingo card, fuel permit, travel permit, log book, and to each question asked I could only reply, 'No sir, don't have that,' or, 'A what?' which seemed to amuse the other drivers in the hut. But the end results could not have been better. The officer said, 'Well, you ain't goin' no place, fella. You're shut down!'

'We can't leave?' I beamed.

'Not 'till you pay me six-hundred-and-forty-three dollars in fines and unload ten thousand pounds of that freight you're running with.'

The six-hundred-and-forty-three dollars in fines he was talking about, we didn't have. The ten thousand pounds of freight he wanted us to unload we weren't about to unload. The truck was packed by hand. It had no pallets that could be lifted by a fork lift. The last items we had put on the truck (and therefore the first off) had taken ten men to load. They were parts of a printing press made of cast iron. I would torch the truck before unloading this. It was time to call New York for sympathy and counsel.

'*Saama! Saama! Saama!*' Izic shouted at me when I told him what was up. 'They can *not* do this! They have *no* right to keep truck at weigh-station! This is *not American!*'

'But, boss, we are ten thousand pounds over,' I pointed out. 'We're not allowed on the road with this much weight. It's, well – illegal.'

'Tsk! Illegal! *This is 'ow we do biz'ness!*' Izic shouted. 'You understand?'

'Absolutely. But it's the law . . .'

'Tell me som'sing. You do as I ask? You go past weigh-station?'

'Yes.'

'Ah – they catch you?'

'That's it.'

'Ass'oles! Lemme speak wiz zem!'

For the first time in six weeks of working I was having fun. With Izic the only pleasure you ever got was to convey bad news. Bad news was anything that would cost him money. For running past a weigh-station in an overweight truck without all these permits and passes, it seemed only fair that it should be this large sum. But so far there was no mention of jail – a disappointment. I was ready for a long nap. I handed the phone to the officer. I could hear Izic beg down the line. Izic was talented at this; but the officer was unmoved. He told Izic we couldn't go anywhere; not until we off-loaded the excess freight. When the officer was finished he handed the phone back to me.

'He is big *ass'ole!*' Izic shouted. There was a pause. He wanted my opinion. I was ready to tell him this steak and potatoes was a saint, a pal, and the only person in authority who had talked any sense in the last three days. But I could not say this so I said nothing.

'Saama, so you must do what you must,' Izic said. 'If you have to rent other truck, rent. Okay? But find me good deal, Saama! And be quick! Customer waiting!'

'Boss,' I said, 'we don't have the money to pay the fine. How are we going to rent a truck?'

'What you talkin' 'bout?' Izic wailed. 'Alon has money! He tell me he has tousand dollar! *Tousand dollar, Saama!* I put five hundred dollar on wire for you . . .'

'But the fine is six-fifty . . .'

'Tsk! Lemme speak wiz Alon.'

I beckoned for Alon to come to the phone. Alon spoke quietly and with great agitation in Hebrew. By the look on his weary face I felt sure he was just about to lose it, which was excellent news. Whilst they spoke the lady trooper

83

appeared. She had been in a back room. She looked despondent. I was not, she informed me, Keith.

I knew this.

She told me young Keith was only a couple of counts short of murder down in Florida. Grand larceny, assault, armed robbery – he was a convicted felon and quite a large catch out here where the big news was who got ticketed for drunk driving on Friday night. But I wasn't him, so she was disappointed. She returned my licence and Alon hung up. He said he would pay the fine. I started ringing the local trucking companies to see if we could rent something and two hours later we had rung every company in Nebraska. There were no trucks to rent. Either they were down in New Mexico on a job, or were axle-deep in pig shit.

The officer had a suggestion. 'Of course,' he said, 'you guys could go into town and put the excess in storage. Then come back and collect it after you off-load in California.'

'Tell me som'sing, please,' said Alon, his eyes dancing all over the place. 'Once we do zis, we have to come back and weigh truck?'

One thing about Israelis, they know opportunity. I knew what my pal was thinking. And as nobody was going to arrest us and throw us in jail, his thinking was potentially the wisest course of action.

The officer said we didn't have to run over the scales again. 'But,' he added, 'if you guys don't do as I say, and I catch you with that load intact, I'll throw you guys in jail so fast your tails won't touch the floor. Then, I'll throw away the key. You understand?'

Perfectly. We called the North Platte Storage Companies, announced loudly we'd be there in an hour, left the weigh-station, and at the first exit we turned off the highway. North Platte two miles to the right, a sign said.

There was no sign for the left. The road pointed at a dirt track. We turned left. In these situations the best policy is to get out of Nebraska fast.

As a matter of general interest I asked Alon what he did in the army.

'I specialize in navigation, Saama.'

This was lucky because some of the roads we had to travel on were not roads at all. They were farm tracks. Miles and miles of dirt. For three hours we didn't see a signpost. We saw coyotes, foxes, chickens, farm animals, but no humans and, more important, no cops.

'This is the life, Saama,' Alon said as we bumped down one dirt track after the next. 'Is really beautiful here!'

I was worried about food and flat tyres. It could be days before we were found. I told him this.

'Is no problem, Saama,' Alon said, lighting up another of his cheroots. 'I show you how to catch snake. Snake is good food. In desert I eat snake all the time.'

I pictured the pair of us chasing around a corn field with a long stick trying to give a feisty diamond head a smack. And I pictured it tagging me. I asked him about this, too.

'Is no problem, Saama. In desert I have many bites. I know cures.'

'But that's an Israeli snake,' I said. 'In America snakes eat towns. Just read Larson.'

'No problem. I keel them.'

In the end it didn't come to chasing snakes in a field. We crossed into the mountain country of Colorado without a flat and without being troubled by the law. Just after nightfall we stopped at a diner north of Denver to eat. We needed to call Izic. We had checked three Western Union offices in the afternoon, but there was no money waiting for us on the wire. Alon's grand was now only a couple of hundred.

This time Alon went to speak with Izic. It was a joy to

see his sorry face come back to the table a while later. Not only had Izic not put money on the wire, he wasn't sure if he could. He was having a cash crisis. This Mr Mysterious Israeli Investor had been detained once again. There would certainly be money waiting for us in California, he claimed, but probably not before. The upshot was Alon would have to pay for gas all the way there, plus food for the both of us. This annoyed Alon more than anything so far. He had saved for this trip so he could buy souvenirs and T-shirts to send home to his brother and family in Israel. Now he couldn't afford even a Doors shirt from Venice Beach, Los Angeles.

'If motherfucker no give me money in Caleyfornia, I keel him,' Alon said.

I had a better idea, but this was no time to bring it up. We cursed Izic through the T-bones and fries and jugs of coffee. Then we discussed the remaining journey. We couldn't stop at another weigh-station. Finding another mutt who would allow us to go to the nearest town and dump the excess freight in storage without a re-run over the scales was improbable. However, the location of the stations were unknown. We asked other truckers in the diner. All of them said weigh-stations were only on the Interstate. So the Interstate was now off limits. We were limited to running only on the back-roads. And we had not yet crossed the Rockies. And even if we could run on the regular highway the truck would have a rough time getting over the mountains with the weight problem, the brake problem, the clutch problem, the light problem and the tyre problem. And another thing: it had started to snow again.

Our only alternative – to climb through a narrow, unploughed back-road pass with snow on the ground, in pitch dark, on roads without a run-off in case of brake failure, or barriers in case you miss a turn here or there, or

86

street-lamps – seemed a mad thing to attempt in the crate we were driving.

'But Saama,' Alon said. 'The Rockies should be really fun, uh?'

Old Alon was a fruit-cake. We tipped the waitress and left.

We circled north of Denver, climbed Rabbits' Ears Pass. It snowed heavily. For six hours we beat the truck up a narrow, steep two-lane switch-back – made for the mountain goat, not old, tired moving truck. At the summit, the cab was smoking from a burnt clutch and visibility of what I hoped was a road (it was between the trees, covered in snow) was down to fifteen feet. As we started to descend it grew worse. There were great banks of cloud, snow and fog. Sometimes I could see no further than the steering wheel. This was bad news for all rabbits and deer.

In all, it took four hours to make the descent. We ran out of brakes twice, T-boned two big eight-point bucks, squashed a number of rabbits, and, for a grand finale, made a 180 into a snow bank. Through all this Alon lay calmly on the bench with his ear-phones in place humming, '*This is the end! My only friend, the end,*' until he realised we weren't moving, then he slipped off the ear-phones and said, 'Saama, you want me to drive?'

'No.'

'You wake me when you tired or som'sing interesting happens, okay?'

Fourteen hours later we had snuck through Colorado, Utah and Nevada, and we were still free men. We had not come to a weigh-station, not popped any more tyres, and not called the boss. We felt like we had outfoxed J. Edgar Hoover himself. But, we were out of money. It was late Sunday afternoon. We had to call the office in New York. Alon would not speak to Izic so I called.

'Where are you, Saama?' Izic asked me.

'Ely, Nevada.'

'*Wha*? Why Nevada? Why you no Caleyfornia?'

I explained that the route we had been forced to take added many hours on to drive time. There was no point telling him about crossing the mountains. If the truck had broken down he would have expected us to gather a pack of wolves and harness them. If the tyres had blown, he would have assumed we would rig make-shift skis to chuss the crate down the mountain to the nearest truck-shop. No feat and certainly no law was expected to defeat the needs of the Bethlehem Moving Man. Besides, I hadn't the energy. In addition to being exhausted and frozen during the night (the heating packed up along with the clutch), during the day the desert had scorched us (law demands air-conditioning in commercial trucks, but Izic did not supply it because he was too cheap). In the course of twelve hours we had gone from Arctic weather to the tropics.

'Tsk! Is really no good,' Izic said. 'Customer waiting. I tell him you be there eigh'-thirty in the morning. You understand? I not happy . . .'

I hung up. We lumbered through the scrub desert country of Nevada stopping at small towns to buy coffee and chocolate bars. When night came the desert cooled and the driving became more comfortable. It was just after 2 a.m. on Monday morning and it looked like we were going to make the customer on time when we passed through Lake Tahoe, a California/Nevada border town, and came to a sign on the road that read: *Department of Agriculture. All Vehicles Must Stop.*

'Saama, Immigration?' Alon asked.

Immigration was Alon's only source of worry. I explained that Agriculture was farm animals. We worked for one, but we weren't carrying any. Alon went back to sleep. I pulled up at the barrier, set the brakes, and not long after, a small Mexican-looking man with jackboots and a bug-green jumpsuit came trotting out of a concrete hut with his arm raised. He came right up to the cab window, put his hands on his hips, looked me in the eye and then spat on the wheel of my truck. It was his way of telling me he didn't mean to take any shit. But I was certain he'd never come across an Israeli moving company before.

'What'cha carryin'?' I was asked.

I told him. He said he'd have to see it for himself, so I jumped down from the cab and took him to the sliding rear door. I was tired but I could see this fellow was going to be a stickler for procedure. Instead of walking next to me, he galloped off ahead, pulling a flashlight from his belt as he went.

The load had shifted against the door so you couldn't open it.

'If that ain' *bullshit!*' the Mexican muttered. He shook his head and spat again, on the mudflap. 'Got a side door?' he asked.

I walked him round the side of the truck and unlocked the Chubb.

'Where's ya Bill of Ladin'?' he asked as I swung the door open.

'Bill of what?'

He spat on my sneaker. 'This is going to be a long night,' he said.

The cargo was invisible; hidden behind a wall of cardboard boxes piled floor to roof. The Mexican climbed up the body-step and tried to push a few of the boxes out the way; but they wouldn't move. He spat on my other shoe.

'So, what kinda furniture you carryin'? Household? Or *garden?*' he asked me.

'Household, I think.'

'Well don't ya *know*, for chrissakes?'

89

'No.'

'Shit.'

I asked him what the difference was and he said, 'Gypsy moths. You come from New York. Now New York is a high-risk area for the gypsy moth. Here, California, we're low risk. Now when you travel from a *high*-risk area to a *low*-risk area you gotta have checks. That's me. I check for the gypsy moth, see? And the garden furniture,' he said, leaning closer, beckoning for my ear, 'is how the gypsy moth travels.'

'That's very interesting.'

The Inspector for Gypsy Moths nodded and then turned and spat again. This time he got a singing cicada and silenced it.

'Well,' he said, 'I'd better see your Bills of Ladin'. Damn, if we ain't gotta lotta work to do.'

He seemed to have forgotten I told him we did not have such a thing. On the off chance we did, I went to wake Alon.

'What he want, Saama?'

'A Bill of Lading.'

Alon shrugged. 'Ga'bidge,' he said. 'I never heard of this.'

Still, there was one possibility. Alon turned on the cab light, opened the glove compartment and pulled out a fistful of what looked like toilet paper. These were the inventory lists for the cargo.

'Maybe is this?' he said, handing them to me.

The lists were written in Hebrew. The names of the clients were not written in full, there were no telephone numbers, no addresses and, unless you could read Hebrew, no furniture. This was not going to please the little man. I took them inside.

The Inspector of Gypsy Moths was sitting at a desk in front of a Mac computer when I walked in. I spread the crumpled lists in front of him and smoothed out the wrinkles.

'So – how many loads ya got?' he asked, not looking up.

There was a steel waste-paper can next to him. His lower lip bulged with tobacco chew. Before I could answer, it deflated and he spat at the can. He missed, but it was sort of interesting.

'Ah, five loads,' I said. 'I think.'

'Well, don't ya *know*??'

I told him there were five. He started counting. Instead of the five inventory lists I claimed to have brought, there were six lists in front of him. He picked up a handful and waved them at me.

'Well,' he shouted, '*which* one ain't meant to be here?'

If I'd known I would have told him but I can't read Hebrew. There was a strong chance these dog-eared scraps were a take-out order from Katz's pastrami deli on Houston. But in these situations, the thing to do is never be daunted. Just as I was about to choose one he threw the whole wad on the table, spat, missed the can, and hit the window. This was too funny and I had to flee the hut in a poorly-disguised fit of coughing.

I ran to the truck and fetched Alon. The evening was about to provide great entertainment. We went back to the hut shortly afterwards, and the Inspector ignored us. He stood by his desk, shaking with anger, pointing at the scraps I had laid out in front of him.

'*Which one*,' he shouted, '*does not belong here?*'

'This one,' I said, pointing at random. 'This one is going to Chicago.'

'Well, *get this shit outta here!*' he screamed, throwing the document over his shoulder. It fluttered to the floor. Alon grinned. Then the Hebrew was discovered.

'Are you kiddin' me?' the Inspector for Gypsy Moths shouted. 'Are you fuckin' kiddin' me? What is this crap?'

91

'Hebrew,' I said.

He was baffled.

'The language of Israel, sir,' I added.

He spat again. He hit a chair. Alon whispered, 'He is really like Arab.'

Then the Inspector had another thought. '*Can you read this shit? . . . Huh? . . . Can you?*' he shouted, thrusting a fist of papers at me. His face was now quite red.

'Yes sir, we can,' I said, trying not to laugh.

'So why's it written in goddamned Hebrew?'

'Because the loads come from Israel, sir. This truck, you see, was packed by Israelis. The Israeli writes like this.'

For a moment this lie seemed to satisfy him. But then his brow furrowed and he had another turn. 'There's no goddamned addresses!' he explained. 'And no names neither! If you ain't got that shit you ain't goin' nowhere!'

We told him we had that shit.

'Well,' he demanded, looking quite white in the face now. 'Where is it? Why ain't it here?'

'Because it's, ummh, out in the truck, sir,' I said.

'What's it doin' in the truck? I need it!' He was almost hysterical – like a customer who has just been told all his furniture has been lost. We had one of those the week before. 'I need it now!' he screamed.

'Is no problem,' Alon said.

We went out to the truck, sat on the bench seat and, in the gloaming of the cab-light, composed fake names and addresses. We scribbled them on the backs of Bethlehem Moving cards and when we had done five cards, we went back inside and put them on his desk above the different inventory lists. Then we took a step back and smiled.

'You guys are really pushing me,' said the Mexican.

We apologised. Next step was to make a legitimate report to the Board of Gypsy Moth Prevention, or whatever, and that meant entering information on the desktop computer, a white plastic Mac, now fired up and ready to use.

The Inspector read aloud, very slow, from the screen: 'Do . . . you . . . wish . . . to . . . start . . . the . . . programme? . . . Yes? . . . Or, no? . . .' It took him a while to articulate this. 'Yes!' the Inspector said. He searched the keys and pressed one. Next question: 'Origin of load?'

'New York,' we said.

'New York. How d'ya spell it?'

I spelled it for him.

'See,' he said, 'if any information is wrongly entered on this computer a whole lotta *shit* comes down on me from the Department, ya understan'?'

'I certainly do.'

He spat again. He missed. We gave him the fake names and addresses. We watched the little green letters appear and then march across the screen in front of him. Alon translated the Hebrew on the lists, and when he got bored he invented things. Whenever important information was missing, we went back out to the truck and made something up.

For two hours we carried scraps of paper back and forth. Sometimes when the strain of keeping a straight face was too much, we fell out the door and coughed and hooted and howled with laughter. The Inspector was too worried about his computer to seem to notice. As the night wore on, the Inspector's aim worsened. By the time he was done with us, there were pools of black tobacco chew by the can, dirty smears on the wall and a couple of hits on the armchair in the corner. Near four-thirty in the morning we were free to enter California.

On each one of our lists he had put a nice pink sticker. 'Impounded for Inspection by the Department of Agriculture,' it read.

93

He kept a copy to give to the Department and we kept a copy to throw out the cab window. The Department was to send Inspectors round to do some inspecting since he couldn't. However, since the addresses we gave him did not exist, nor the customers, they weren't going to have much luck.

'Don't you guys ever show up through here again with this shit!' the Inspector for Gypsy Moths grumbled as we climbed up into the cab and he lifted the gate. 'Cuz next time, next time I'll have you fuckers locked up!'

And with all due justification, I'd say. We said good night, thanked him for all his help, wished him happiness in all things, and drove off just as the light was starting to break on the Sierras.

Eight o'clock the following morning we arrived in Lincoln, California. It was a small, sleepy town set an hour north and east of San Francisco. We checked the Western Union office to see if there was any money waiting for us. We had three dollars left. There was no money. We called Izic. There was no Izic. Just an answer machine: ''Allo. This is Bethlehem Moving and Storage Company. I am sorry no one is in office. If you have a move and want us, please leave name and number for to call. Thank you.'

I looked at Alon, standing by me at the phone. 'Now tell me Mexico isn't a good idea.'

Alon grinned. 'Maybe, Saama,' he said.

We didn't go to Mexico in the end. Izic sent us money and I spent that summer on the road for him. I went across to California eight times, down to Florida and the Keys twice and made a number of runs out to Chicago and Saint Louis. America was my back garden that summer and the cab was my home. Sometimes I ran loads across on my own, sometimes I'd have a partner. I saw many fine things driving around the country. I saw the Holy Rollers Rig, a tractor-trailer with a church in the back. It was on this rig that I met JTD. JTD was a chihuahua and his real name was Jesus Trucking Dog. A husband-and-wife team ran the rig. The husband had seen the Lord one night on the road thirty years earlier. The Lord had told him to make a chapel for truckers, and to move around the country spreading the Word, so he did.

I learnt to lie to Izic to get sleep claiming flat tyres, drug searches, or whatever else popped into the noodle if I didn't feel like driving the twenty-four hours a day he wanted, or I wanted to make a detour to see some sight I had not yet seen.

I ran the truck up the coast road of California twice at night during the summer and one time, in San Simeon, Hurst's hometown, Alon showed me how to find the north pole star. Coming through the mountain country of Four Corners and out into the desert during a full moon and night sky made the spirit soar. I always tried to make a stop in Gallup, New Mexico during daylight hours on the way across the I. 40 because the shops there were so full of decent things. I bought myself an orange velvet Indian shirt with a collar the size of a canoe. I never went back through Lake Tahoe. When I crossed the California border I never mentioned I was carrying furniture, the post on the road into LA being the easiest, especially before dawn. In Colorado I learnt always to wash and shave before I pulled into the weigh-stations because they were the most safety-conscious, with the Rockies ahead.

On the last trip across for the both of us, Alon and I were on our way back from San Francisco, having driven across the Mojave, when we were stopped at an immigration check-point on the road outside of Sierra Blanca, Texas, near midnight. Alon was lifted from the truck and put under arrest. For two hours I waited to hear from him

95

but they kept him in the hut. I didn't know which lie he was going to tell them, so I stayed in the cab. After a long while I went into the hut and asked the officials what they planned on doing to him and they said, 'He's going off to camp to chip rocks.'

Alon grinned. 'Don't worry, Saama,' he said. 'Nothing will be as bad as Israeli Army, or Bethlehem!' That was the last I saw of him. But I wasn't too worried for him. He was more than capable of looking after himself and had the rare ability of finding every situation in life interesting, good or bad. In the end I got word from Izic that after three weeks in a deportation camp in El Paso, Texas, Alon got the authorities to deport him – to Brazil, where he was going to sit on a beach and write poetry. That's what he'd wanted to do all summer, and where I believe he still is, sitting under a palm tree, thinking of Mr Jim Morrison and writing beautiful poems.

Coming into the fall I'd had my fill of the road and I quit. The last time I saw Izic was when I went up to his office in December of that year, just before Christmas, to collect four thousand dollars he still owed me.

As it was, I happened to walk in on the middle of something. There was an old black man standing in the office whom Izic had picked up off the street and had offered five dollars to if the man could perform a simple chore. But when Izic saw me walk into his office, he threw up his arms and said, 'My friend! Thanks be to God you are here! Come! Please! Sit!'

The old black fellow was hustled out the office and I was put in an office chair in his place.

I asked what this was all about and Izic gave me a slip of paper on which was written: a) Hallo! This is Bank Leumi, John speaking. How can I help you please? b) I am the manager of Bank Leumi. c) Hold one minute please! First I must have customer's name and account number!

d) Yes! There is no problem with Bethlehem's account. The cheque is good. e) Thank you! Have a nice day!

'I have a truck stuck in garage in Los Angeles,' Izic told me mournfully. 'Very important I get truck . . .'

At that same moment the phone rang. Izic hushed for silence. I was given the receiver.

'Hello,' said a voice, 'is this Bank Leumi?'

So Izic had given the poor sucker at a truck-shop in Los Angeles the telephone number of his bank – an extension line in the office. I looked over at Izic and mouthed the words, 'four grand'.

Izic nodded his head furiously and held his hands together as if he was begging. I told the man this was indeed Bank Leumi and asked how I could help him.

'Well, I wonder if you can. I am calling from Los Angeles and I have a client who banks with you and wants to write me a company cheque for two-and-a-half thousand dollars for some work I have done on his truck. I'd like to know if his cheque is good.'

I asked for the particulars of the cheque and the account number and put the man on hold. After a minute I came back to the phone and told the garage owner there would be no trouble with it. The man then asked if Bethlehem ever had a credit problem with the bank.

'A credit problem?' I asked, watching Izic hop up and down making imploring gestures. 'No, sir,' I said. 'Never.' And with that the man hung up.

Izic jumped with joy, hugged me, called me his brother and told me I'd really helped him, that he'd pay the man back next week, only he needed the truck back in New York by Tuesday for some big commercial job they had just been given. We had nothing much more to say. Izic was busy trying to get a new business off the ground: raising money to lease a fleet of tractor-trailers to haul food and clothes across country for another Israeli. So he went into the back room and came back with a cheque. I told him I would only take cash.

'Saama,' he said. 'You finally learn something, huh?'

I went home to 29th Street with all my money – a surprise – and that night I went down to El Quijote on 23rd Street, with the boys, to celebrate.

Some years later I passed the office on 8th Avenue and stopped to ring the bell. Bethlehem had moved or gone bankrupt, the office was again an apartment – as it was meant to have been when Izic used it as an office. The lady didn't know where they had gone or if they were still in business. These days I never see the trucks on the streets of Manhattan and it's been a long time since I heard from Alon, Ya-ir, Gideon, Mickey, Ran, Eli and the others. But I wish them all well. And you too, Izic. You crooked bastard.

Four

That winter there was a cold snap in Manhattan that lasted about six months. We had guests come visit all winter. I got letters from Carla telling me about her life down in Florida and she sent me a picture of her baby boy. She said she was bored, she needed something to do. Her husband worked late and she thought he had a drinking problem. We wrote often and I told her what was going on with myself, what faces had come into town, what faces had left. Nothing had changed. She said she wanted to come up and stay. I told her that wasn't such a good idea. I didn't hear from her for a long time after that.

By the time Spring rolled around, the birds chirped, and the feet had started to thaw again, I was up to the eye-teeth with snow flurries, Arctic winds, iced pavements, slush in the sneakers, pipes that wouldn't incubate a roach, and pay-cheques that barely covered the rent. I had a job working for corporate caterers.

Then one night I was in a bar with two friends, watching something on TV called *Spring Break*. What a perfect monument to teen. Ten thousand Joe-college types in Daytona, Florida judging beauty contests, riding around in convertibles listening to rock bands, bungee jumping and dating. After winter in Manhattan, *Spring Break* looked like the Pearly Gates for a man with money worries and damp sneakers.

'Jeez!' said my friend Paul Lennon, an Irishman, putting

his glass down. 'Don't dem look like they could do with a little som't'ing on their backs to keep the poor lambs warm? I mean – *look* at that wind! He's dressed but they got nut'in on!'

The presenter wore a tropical shirt with a parrot or two. The girls on either arm,wore bikinis.

'What those girls need is one of my T-shirts,' said Paul, laughing innocently.

Paul and his lady ran a small clothes store over on 6th Street. They sold clothes to Manhattan's nightbirds. A tiny part of the current vision was their swing on the T-shirt.

'They certainly do,' I said. 'And know what? Daytona is an entrepreneur's paradise. Just look at it. All those kids down there, right after exams, wanting to spend money and have fun. We should get down there and sell something.'

'A road trip,' said Buster. 'I'd rather like that.'

'What would you sell?' asked Paul.

'Your T-shirts,' I said.

And suddenly, like that – it took no more with the currents all flowing in union towards Florida and the bright sunshine – we were heads down, over the beer, discussing why we should jump into Buster's vintage Cadillac Brougham d'Elegance, roll over to Paul's store, pick up some of his top-of-the-line sportswear shirts, pick up some pizza from John's Best, then lay a course for the Holland Tunnel, the I.95 and the south, to join the rest of young America.

The idea had a lot going for it. Buster had money; Paul had merchandise; the d'Elegance had a full tank; the rent was due soon; I was broke; more important, we might not only finance the whole venture – motels, gas, food, entertainments, and drink – but could also turn a profit. *Spring Break* was a business opportunity.

By late afternoon the next day we had made plans. Ten o'clock that night we were flying down the Jersey Turnpike, the needle of the d'Elegance buried somewhere near the oil lamp, the wipers struggling with the snow, the heating up full, the car fish-tailing gently, and all sorts of unnatural things happening to the '79 vintage automobile.

Lamps, all of them, were lighting up on the console and blinking: Level Ride, Generator, Oil, and a few I couldn't read because of the dirt. We ignored them. Then the headlamps packed up somewhere near the Delaware River, not far from the state line, and we slewed into a Roy Rogers and slid to a shuddering halt. We feared this to be the end; but a wipe of the headlamps fixed things. Now properly illuminated we stormed through the night, taking shifts at the wheel, roaring over the snowy Potomac, slicing through Maryland, Virginia, the Carolinas and by lunch the next day we were down in Savannah, Georgia, in a bar, in the old town, by the river, where out the window we saw red tugs pass by under a grey, blustery sky.

The barlady was young and pretty. She took a shine to young Buster. He asked her to come with us.

'Have you back by Sunday,' he told her. 'On my honour.'

But this girl was no fool. She said she didn't believe a word of it. So we left.

Six-thirty that night I was standing at a petrol pump, pumping high test into the d'Elegance, on the outskirts of Daytona, twelve hundred miles now from New York City. There was a warm wind on my arms, and a clear blue sky above. The boys were inside the convenience store. I heard rubber squeals and raucous rock'n'roll. I looked out the gas lot, over at the boulevard, where the traffic was passing slowly under the tall palms, and I saw a hot pink open-top jeep filled with long-haired, pretty young blondes, in bikini tops. They wore neon-coloured bicycle shades; they danced in their seats and what I liked most was they waved as

101

they passed. At me. As I pumped gasoline into the d'Elegance.

I went in to tell the boys about this when I'd finished. I told them we were in the right place and this was going to be a hell of a time for us. I was sure of it.

The old roasted pecan from behind the till must have been listening, because when I went over to pay him he looked up and cracked a smile and said, 'If what you want is Spring Breakers, where you're gonna have to go is the Strip. That's where they all go. The Strip.'

A half hour later, around seven in the evening now on this Friday night, palm trees waving in the neon sunset, warm air blowing through the open windows, we sat in traffic three lanes thick, surrounded by collegiates. Thousands of them. Everywhere you turned: in cars; spilling over the pavements; running and whooping out of bars; queuing up at restaurants; unloading at hotels. It was something the like of which I had never seen before.

We crawled past the gift stores, the sun-oil shacks, the big theme hotels, the signs saying *Daytona Welcomes Spring Breakers*!, the restaurants, night-clubs and fast food stores. We watched gangs of water-fighters squat in the flat-beds of fluorescent-coloured pick-ups, armed with the Super Soaker 200 pump-action water cannon. We saw them dance in their seats, juggle their brown bodies, and tap out the beat of Latino Disco, Techno, House, Rap, Rock and Salsa. We saw them smoke their tyres and pop roll-on power wheelies on the big, one litre, Jap sports cycles. And some of them had come from as far away as Nebraska.

After a couple of turns back and forth we parked the d'Elegance at the Seafarer Restaurant for dinner. The bar was full and noisy. Teenagers watched the college basketball finals on the TVs around the bar. The restaurant in the back was filled to capacity with more of the same eating surf'n'turf'n'fries. No one here was over twenty-two.

102

The men were pumped-up, red-faced, bow-backed, thick-necked, wearing cut-off T-shirts to best advertise their proud muscles. The young girls were middle American looking: LA gear, shorts, sports bra, frosted blonde hair and bangs. But they all wore T-shirts. A good sign for salesmen of super-fabulous New York sportswear. We took a table at the rear.

Two University of Miami weight-lifters hulked past. A young waitress arrived with the beer. Paul Lennon asked the girl where we would find the action for the night.

'What are you looking for?'

'A club,' said Paul Lennon. 'The best nightclub in town.'

'The Coliseum,' the girl said.

An hour later, Buster was snoring peacefully in the Brougham's sleeping quarters on the rear seats. We walked down the road to the club. But once close we saw a long line outside. We stood to one side for a minute. 'Got an idea,' I said. I told Paul and he said 'Wurf a try.' Paul rehearsed it and when we were ready we went up to the glass doors, ahead of the long lines to where this big man with four-ply chest hair stood collecting tickets.

'Ehm,' said Paul. 'Are you the manager?'

'Yeah, what can I do for you, guys?'

'Well,' said Paul Lennon. 'We're down here on be'alf of Billy Idol.'

'Who?' said the man, taking a ticket.

'Billy Idol,' said Paul Lennon. 'De fokin' rock star.'

'Oh, sure. I know Billy Idol.'

'Good. Well, Billy hired me and my partner here to shoot the video for his next hit, *Spring Break*, so we was down scoutin' locations and was wantin' to look at your club to see if we could shoot som'ting for Billy you know. For his next video. On the MTV . . .'

103

The man said nothing. He lifted his eyebrows which were joined right the way across his forehead.

'Look,' said Paul, 'I gotta lotta places to see dis'evening so I'll get to the fokin' point. We don't want to queue and, ehm, we don't want to pay – how d'you feel about that?'

'For a Billy Idol video?'

'The same.'

Paul Lennon smiled and scratched the top of his head. The manager looked at me and then at Paul. Paul was impressive: foundry boots, black leather jeans, torn T-shirt, black leather motor-cycle jacket, short orange Ken Doll hair. Paul had himself a look.

'All right. Sure.'

So we got in skipping the line and not paying a cent. From that moment on we were convinced we had the measure of this fine town.

Buster was still asleep when we got back to the d'Elegance, a few hours later, ears ringing from the din of loud music. We hopped on the highway, headed south one exit to New Smyrna, then lumbered through the unlit streets of bungalows and ranch houses and gardens, past darkened boarding houses, trying to find a place to stay for the night, believing the hotels on the Strip would charge us too much. But everywhere we drove we came across No Vacancy signs or moteliers who did not want the custom of Spring Breakers, even though we tried to convince them we weren't. At one place, Paul rang the bell and a man in a cotton vest came out and said, 'Are you Adam Clayton of U2?'

'No, I'm Paul Lennon of Dublin.' We didn't get that room either.

We stopped at an empty diner for a burger. Then we heard about the Shangri-La Motel on Route 1, courtesy of a pump attendant at the Exxon Station.

We drove to it and pulled under the thatched shade by

the sign swinging loose on one chain. I rang the bell. An old man with fifties glasses and stubble showed us to two rooms for seventy-four dollars cash, two double beds a room. The d'Elegance was parked in the rear. The bags were brought in. Then we slept.

Next morning I was woken by the noise of traffic. I dressed and went outside. It was hot and blue. Across the street was a Harley-Davidson parts and accessories store. As I stood and looked around and listened to the cicadas, the air started to spit and crackle down the street. Electra-Glides, a pack of eight of them, chromed and gleaming with custom shop paint jobs, raked fronts, studded leather saddlebags, and highway bars rolled right past, sedately, and in lane. Leather ladies were riding these cycles. Not a minute later, more women came past from the opposite direction. In convertibles and in the flatbeds of pick-up trucks. Daytona, I thought. Look at it. What a place.

I banged on Buster's door. I woke Paul. We paid the man for another night and headed down Route 1, past the grass airfield with the signs by the roadside advertising rides in crop-dusters for seven bucks. An old biplane climbed off the strip, trailing a long streamer advertising a wet T-shirt contest at Big Kahuna's, 3 o'clock that afternoon.

Paul Lennon stuck his pasty white arm out the window into the sunshine, put on a tape, and laughed. 'This is all right, you know,' he said.

We went north – past the tall swamp grass, over a bridge where new pick-ups were parked on the dirt, and fishermen stood in the sun with their rods over the water – following the signs for Daytona.

We drove to the Strip to find a place for breakfast; but the Strip was too busy so we carried on driving to see what there was until we came to a place called Ponce Inlet. We stopped near a red lighthouse where an old shack of a restaurant overlooked a wooden dock, some game fishing boats, and out through the tall-grass channels, the Atlantic, and Cape Canaveral.

We sat at a table in the shade of a twisted swamp oak that was growing up through the outside deck. The waitress brought us a pitcher of dark beer with a cupful of ice floating in it. She was a friendly girl and told us the good places to go out if we wanted more mature surroundings. We ordered some grouper and some Mahi sandwiches, and fries. Ten minutes later the waitress came back with another pitcher. A man in a red shirt had just come in the place and bought the whole bar a round.

'Nice of him,' said Paul Lennon, laughing.

That afternoon we went down to the Strip and paid three dollars to take the d'Elegance onto the beach. A highway had been set up down the white sand. As we rode along the empty part of the beach towards the pier a couple of miles away, a flight of pelicans swooped down over the tops of the waves looking for fish. High above them, a chain of old bi-planes droned by in the blue sky.

We parked by the pier, opened up the trunk, and no sooner had we laid the T-shirts on the boot than I saw we were going to have a problem with the merchandise. The shirts were not right.

'What d'you mean they're not right?' Paul Lennon asked.

After a night and half a day in the town I had begun to notice the consumer in Daytona wore T-shirts with things like: JUST GIVE ME YOUR PHONE NUMBER. Not: CHOICE, which is politically correct and popular with the earnest, urban types, but no good to us as businessmen. I told him this. I had a feeling the material, black rayon, was going to be about as popular as a bar that didn't sell beer. Your nightbird of New York likes the feel of black rayon, but not homophobic college kids. And the sizes. Made for transvestites not beefy bully boys. I said all this. Paul Lennon shrugged and picked at his tooth.

But we tried. We harangued every vehicle that came past, without success. Then a cop on an ATV bike stopped to ask us what we were doing. I told him. He asked if I had a permit.

'No, sir.'

'Can't sell nothing unless you have a permit from the City of Daytona.'

We packed up the shirts. The officer rode off on his bike. 'Never mind,' I said. 'We can try some of the stores.'

But no store wanted them.

'Wrong time of day,' Paul said. 'Wear 'em to a night-club. Then they'll understand. Nights is for us.'

So we went off to watch the bungee jumpers on the front. A 240 pound gorilla was being hoisted up in the cage to jump just as we arrived. But he lost his nerve and had to be brought down again. The crowd jeered. We moved on. We watched the kids on the jet-skis ride the surf; then kicked around a ball on the sand at the empty part of the beach and later, stopped into Kahuna's to listen to a reggae band chant, 'Why drink and drive when you can smoke and flyyyy!'

After eating we hit the clubs in the hotels on the Strip. We hustled to make some sales, but none of the girls wanted our T-shirts. What the girls wanted was drink, lots of drink.

'Have to be philosophical about it,' said Buster as we drove back to New Smyrna, at near two in the morning. 'We're just going to have a good time, that's all.'

He put on Mr Neil Young. Old Man. Very peaceful. For about three minutes.

Then, in the rear-view, I saw a flashing rack of blue lights. I pulled the d'Elegance over and waited.

A moment later a patrolman came up to the car. I was

stopped, he said, because I was driving too close to another vehicle. Hard to avoid in traffic in a 30 mph zone. He asked for my licence. I gave it to him. He went away and when he came back he said, 'Your licence has been suspended. Step out the automobile, please. And take it slow.'

Now why should my licence be suspended, I wondered in my wobbly, narcotic fug. I could only conclude it was for skipping through a weigh-station without a log book, an inventory list, a fuel tax certificate and a few other things over in California, the year before, when I was working for Izic. Izic had promised me he had looked after it on my behalf. But Izic must have thrown my ticket in the trash. Now it was on the computers here in Port Orange.

The patrolman wrote me a ticket for driving whilst under suspension. I was asked to show the car documents. I told Buster. He fetched them from the glove compartment and handed them out the window.

'Have you been drinking?' the officer asked me.

'Only a few beers.'

'Step over here please. I'd like to give you a sobriety test.'

So I took this test and passed, which was quite something. I felt this brutal, unwarranted interruption to our peace was about to finish. No chance. The officer asked me if I had any objections to having him and his partner search the automobile. I said no.

This search revealed Paul Lennon dozing in the back seat.

'What in hell is he doing asleep?' the cop shouted at Buster, who was now also out the car.

'Well,' said Buster, yawning. 'He's tired. It's two in the morning.'

This was suspicious and highly criminal. 'Wake him up!' the cop shouted. 'Wake him up now!'

'O Paul!' called Buster. 'Pau-l!'

Paul came stumbling out the rear door of the d'Elegance into a phalanx of armed policemen and shining flashlights.

'What d'fock . . .' said Paul, putting his hands above his head rapidly. Paul Lennon looked just like a lamped leather rabbit.

'Got stopped,' said Buster. 'Nothing to worry about.'

'Jeez,' said Paul.

'Shut the fuck up!' said the cop.

We were told to go stand by a fence. A drug unit arrived. A dog was put in the car. Not long after I was summoned.

'This is marijuana,' the officer said, holding up a roach. 'I found it in the ashtray. D'you know where it came from?'

'No.'

'D'you take responsibility?'

'No.'

'Does it belong to you? Or d'you know who it belongs to?'

'No.'

'I'm placing you under arrest.' Night night, Neil Young.

In the back of the Port Orange police cruiser, wrists cuffed behind my back, I remembered we had paid for a second night at the Shangri-La. Seventy-four fucking dollars. And we hadn't sold one T-shirt that day. Lord, it's hard to make a buck.

'What's your philosophy about this, then?' asked Paul Lennon – when he and Buster were slung in next to me.

'Just a formality,' said Buster. 'They'll let us go once we get to the station.'

Bob's Auto arrived. The d'Elegance was winched up onto the bed.

'How much is it going to cost to get back our car . . .' I started to ask the two officers when they got in the cruiser.

'Shut up!' I was quoted.

The two officers said, just to make us feel worse, that had we been driving an automobile with local plates, not

New York plates, they would have let us off with just a citation. As it was, the car was going off to the pound where it would cost us God knew what to get it back, and we were off to the station to get stuck in a cell for the night before going to see the judge in the morning on two charges: driving a car with a suspended licence, and possession of marijuana under twenty grams. Blatant discrimination. Pure and simple. We were in a dangerous, bigoted country.

After getting to the jailhouse, we were stripped of possessions, finger-printed, mug-shot and slung in separate cells for three and a half hours. Then we were cuffed again, and taken by a young lady officer, at illegal speeds for the common road user, on a trip to . . .

'Miss, where are we . . .'

'Shut up back there!'

Signs on the highway, announcing the services of bail bondsmen, flashed past the windows either side. The car slowed from about ninety-five to almost the speed limit and made a violent turn off the highway past a sign: *Volusia County Department of Correction.*

O boy. So this was where they were taking us humble T-shirt salesmen: the County. Driving along past some nicely manicured lawns, there was a sight to make the old teeth rattle – a prison compound, with watchtowers, high electrocuted wire, a windowless city-block-sized building, with a recreational area with big free weights, a squat board, and a bench press facility, which was, no doubt, used by sex-fiends, killers and rapists. But that is all right, I thought. I have been to Public School in England. There, parents will pay good money to send a kid to places like this.

The compound slipped past. We pulled around the side, to a sliding gate at the car port: prisoner reception and greetings area.

110

'Prisoners for processing,' said the blonde driver to the speaker by her open window. The gate slid open, we drove in. Not long after we were in the belly of the beast standing with our hands still cuffed behind us, as uncomfortable as it always is when the wrists are swollen from alcohol poisoning.

A prisoner came down the drab corridor as we waited. He was in blue overalls and had the jail-cut hairstyle and Imperial beard arrangement that makes any man look like a homicidal maniac. He came past us in foot manacles, slowly pushing a laundry basket. He stared at us. He had a smile on his lips. He did not blink. I think he was being friendly.

Buster was first to be entered. He had the cuffs removed, was frisked again, was asked to sign a yellow form marked INMATE PERSONAL PROPERTY RECORD, then had his pockets emptied.

The guard checked Buster behind the ears, under the tongue, between the cheek and gum of upper and lower jaw with a gloved hand; fingerprinted him again; tagged him with a plastic wrist band that read VOLUSIA COUNTY DEPARTMENT OF CORRECTION #284232 and took him off for a mug-shot with the polaroid behind a screen, nearby.

All this seemed a little too officious and wasteful of the state's precious time. We were going to be let out in a couple of hours. I said to the guard, 'You know, there's really no need to waste your precious time doing all of this, because when the judge sees us in a few . . .'

'You ain't gonna see no judge today,' said the guard. 'You missed the cut.'

'This,' said Paul Lennon, 'is turning into a *night*mare.'

Buster was taken off to a holding cell down the concrete corridor. A big black female prisoner, foot-shackled, came

111

past in an orange jumpsuit and I thought: look, jails must be co-ed down here. This is progressive.

But then I looked closely at this big girl and decided she looked more trouble than most men, so this wasn't much of a consolation.

Paul Lennon's fingers were rolled in the ink, then put on the sheet for printing. His foundry boots were judged as dangerous weapons and were taken from him. Instead he was given white plastic shower slippers, which matched the new colour of his face.

'Excuse me, sir,' I said to the man processing Paul. 'Is there any way we can get let out – if we got a lawyer, public defender or . . .'

'Get a bondsman,' he said. 'He can post the sixteen hundred dollar bond and you guys can walk. Otherwise, you're in here 'till Monday, Tuesday, Wednesday – whenever the judge gets round to seeing you.'

'So how do we get a bondsman?'

'There's a phone in the holding cell and a list in the window.'

Well, this was the answer then, I thought. Ring a bondsman and give him sixteen hundred dollars. But to do this, very early on a Sunday morning, from a holding pen at the county jail on a phone that would, according to the guard, only make reverse charge calls, posed a few problems. I had no money. Carla might have money, but her husband was most likely in bed with her. Calling the pair of them would not do if the operator had to say, 'I have a reverse charge call from the Volusia County Jail – would you accept the charges?' at six o'clock on a Sunday morning from an ex-boyfriend, a graduate of Carla's voluptuous charms. Hubby, you see, was a jealous man, according to the letters. Back at 29th Street, no-one would pick up the phone, and no-one had any money anyway. Everybody else I knew was broke. This sixteen hundred dollars was going to be difficult to find. Maybe the bondsman would take T-shirts instead.

I punched in the numbers and time after time was told my call was not accepted. No bondsman seemed to be at work at this early hour. Buster lay on the bench, singing. Buster was still drunk.

I worked down the list. Paul read the numbers aloud. Fifteen calls later we rang *Ace Bail Bonds, Inc.* (437-HELP, 24-Hour Service), and found Scotty. I explained our little problem. Scotty said we needed two things: money, and a signature of someone who would sign for us. But they couldn't come from New York. 'We're focked,' said Paul Lennon, putting his head in his hands.

The cell door opened. Breakfast was given to us. It looked like the sort of thing dog-owners in Manhattan bend down to pick up with a baggy. The trays were put back by the door.

Then Buster had a good idea. 'You know,' he said, 'I think I know someone I could call who would help us.'

'You're a champ,' I said. 'What's the number?'

'Well, let me see now. It's in my address book and, oh. They've got that.'

I yelled for the guard. The guard fetched the book. Buster made some calls. The third try he found a friend. The friend was so impressed and concerned that a nice young man like Buster could be in such terrible danger, teetering on the threshold of rape and savagery, that he offered to give us as much help as possible, put money on the wire from New York, call Scotty at 437-HELP, rustle up an out-of-state signature, be our Operational Head-quarters and spearhead our defence and future liberation. At six on a Sunday morning.

'We're saved!' said Paul Lennon.

But then we heard the clank of jailor's keys echo in the

113

outside corridor. The door opened and the guard said, 'Lennon! You're first. We gotta process you.'

'What? Why *me*? Where are you taking . . .'

'Just come with me, Lennon.'

We tried explaining to the jailor, a woman, that we were in the midst of organising our defence, and the arrival of our bondsman with the money to fund this great institution was imminent.

'I don't want to hear any of your shit,' she said. 'Follow me.'

Paul was led away.

From then on, each time we heard the jailor's keys rattle in the concrete corridors, we rushed for the phone and started blabbing, hoping to postpone the inevitable until the bondsman got down to the jail to spring us.

The cell door opened again whilst Paul was gone. A young, dishevelled man with curly hair, a pot-belly, a *Gators* T-shirt, jeans and dirty cross-trainers was put amongst us.

'Fuckin' assholes!' said the young man. He collapsed on the bench next to Buster. He stank of booze.

We asked him what he'd done to be in here with us. He said he'd had quite a night. He'd rammed his Trans-Am into the back of a parked car when drunk, attempted to flee the scene, was chased at high speed all around Port Orange, was caught, searched, and found to have in his possession a half ounce of grass.

'And I had overshot my driveway by just six feet! *Six feet*! Fuck, if I had made that those cocksuckers wouldn't have got my ass. What d'they get you for?'

'A roach,' I said.

'Ha ha ha,' said the *Gators* fan. 'Ha ha ha. Now tell me the truth.'

'This is the truth.'

'Fuckin' assholes.'

114

We watched him go to the phone. He dialled a number, then said, 'This is Todd. At the County. Hello? Yeah, it's Todd. Is dad there? Yeah, I'm in jail. Uh-huh – Three-and-a-half thousand. Yeah. He what? What d'you mean he doesn't want to talk to me? Hello? Hello? Hello?'

He banged the phone down on the receiver. 'Fuckin'' assholes!' he said. He came over, slumped on the bench next to us, and sprawled out. In a few minutes he was fast asleep.

The keys jangled in the corridor outside and Buster dived for the phone. The door opened, Paul Lennon was returned. The jailor asked me to join her for processing and I pointed at the phone and told her I was just talking to the bondsman and . . .

'I'll be back,' she said.

Buster called Scotty. Scotty said he was waiting on the money. The door opened again and another man was thrown amongst us. He was in his twenties, scruffy, had grey slacks, greasy hair, spectacles with a band-aid holding an arm in place, a dress shirt, and was arrested, he said, for violating his parole. They had come to his house a half hour earlier.

'Nobody's fokin' safe,' said Paul Lennon. 'Fascists. I mean, Jesus, from your own bed.'

The keys jangled again, the door opened, and Paul and I were plucked from the cell and marched off for the final stage of processing, leaving Buster talking enthusiastically to nobody at all on the telephone.

We were separated.

'Take your clothes off,' said the guard.

'Why?' I asked.

'Shower time, my friend.'

I undressed.

'Man,' said the guard to me as I stepped out of my

115

palomino boxers, 'where did you get them motherfuckin' funny-ass cow shorts?'

'A gift.'

'Weirdest motherfuckers I *ever* did see.'

Scrubbed, I was given a change of clothing: a bright duck-hunter's-orange jumpsuit with VCDC printed on the back. The first orange suit was too short.

'Doesn't matter,' I said. 'I won't be in long.'

'That's what they all say,' said the guard.

I was given a bigger convict's uniform, then taken along a different set of corridors and put in another holding pen. Paul Lennon was waiting.

'Nightmare,' he said. 'I just can't. I can't. Jesus.'

Unlike the other holding pen this one was narrow and deep, with no window. It had a steel toilet and sink, painted breeze-blocks, and two long wooden benches.

Soon after we were joined by Buster, also with a change of clothes. Then a big man with a beard and ice-blue eyes was thrown in. And finally the newcomer with the band-aid spectacles, expert on the laws of the County.

'I hope we stay here all morning,' said Paul, as we all sat in silence. 'This ain't so . . .'

The door opened again. 'All of you!' the guard shouted. 'Move out!'

We were marched out into the corridor.

'Line up in pairs!'

The guard unfurled a long chain. He laid it on the floor. On this snake were seven sets of handcuffs, and some foot shackles for the seventh man. The guard bolted us together in pairs. The kid with the broken spectacles got the foot shackles.

We were taken down a warren of corridors to the car port and put in a cage, in the back of a white beaten-up Chevy Econoline.

116

I introduced myself to the big man who was bolted next to me. 'Nice to meet you,' I said. 'And you are?'

'Karl.'

'So, Karl,' I said. 'Have you ever been here before?'

He shook his head. I introduced my friends. We shook. Like proper gentlemen. With handcuffs.

The van ferried us over to the compound. The man with the broken glasses laughed all the way.

The van stopped and we were unloaded. We came tripping out two-by-two, passed through another couple of airlock doors and soon stood by a counter and bullet-proof lexan arrangement that housed an ox of a man, in grey prison officer's uniform, called Mr Williams. I knew this because he said, 'My name is Mr Williams. You will call me Mr Williams. Or sir! Whatever I want you to do, you will do – *do you understand*?'

'Yes, Mr Williams, sir!' we saluted and shouted.

'Good.'

As we were uncuffed and unshackled, a middle-aged, balding, overweight Italian in jeans and cowboy boots was led to the desk. He wore a leather waistcoat and a T-shirt.

This man, who looked like Joe Pesci, was so excited to be getting out, he tore off the plastic bracelet from his wrist with his prisoner's ID#. Mr Williams smiled. Mr Williams sent the prisoner back to his cell for the next couple of hours to cool his heels.

Unshackled, we were called to the window one by one, to sign another INMATE PERSONAL PROPERTY RECORD; then told to go down the corridor and into the first room to pick out a bedding roll. Bedding roll under one arm, we were given a plastic mug, toothbrush, toothpaste, soap, and a pamphlet on prison etiquette for new boys. Most civil. Now we were matriculated.

'Right,' said Mr Williams when we were all lined up, outfitted, and equipped for our stay, 'follow the officer!'

117

In double file, we were led down another warren of concrete corridors, under banks of fluorescent lights. We didn't pass one window to the outside, anywhere. We arrived at the security hub for the whole place. A guard sat behind a circular desk, chewing tobacco. The guard dispatched us all to D Block. We were walked off. Outside what looked like a large decompression chamber, we came to a halt.

The guard started to read our names out from a list with bunk allocations. The guard came to Paul. 'Lennon,' he said. 'Lennon, are you all right? You don't look well.'

Paul Lennon had been mute for a while. Now he stood with his shoulders slumped, scratching his chin, blinking.

'Is it stress, Lennon?'

Here we were in the belly of the drab beast and he was asking the smallest man amongst us if he was feeling a little stressed at entering a place with a worse reputation than Madonna.

'Ah. Ah, well. Ah, ehm,' Paul muttered.

The guard looked at him for a minute longer, decided he must be all right and activated the doors. The first door slid open mechanically. We walked into the airlock. The door slid to behind us. Then the door in front opened mechanically. We stepped through it, into a brightly-lit room. The door closed silently behind us.

First thing I saw was a pair of friendly transvestites playing Monopoly at one of the tables arranged in front of the TV set. One was fifty, chubby, and had the same hairstyle as my dear Gran. His boyfriend was a teenager with a bad skin condition; probably due to prison food. They smiled.

I smiled. Nobody else in the place was interested in us. There were about twenty men in D Block. It had great facilities. Better than school: TV, newspapers, phone – all for our entertainment. The only problem was that the TV was tuned to the Florida Golf Classic and the room was full of golf nuts.

D Block was laid out like a study hall – even the colour was the same, a pale lime blue. It was flanked in an L by two floors of cells – D 1-9 was lower level, and D 10-18 was the upper – with two beds, a toilet and a sink per cell. There were showers at either end and a number of tables facing a TV. The floors were bare concrete. The only view in the place was of C Block, across the way. In C Block there were more prisoners doing exactly what this lot were doing – nothing.

The gents in our block were mostly white, middle-aged, listless and not particularly fierce. About ten sat at the tables watching the TV, or reading the Daytona papers. The others were asleep in their cells. All cell doors were open. We went down to the lower level of cells to dump our bedding rolls on our bunks.

After fifteen minutes of it I'd seen enough. What to do? Our pro, the legal expert with broken glasses, in D4 upper, went straight to bed. Buster and Paul sat outside their cells and played the longest game of chess in history. I read two papers and then called 437-HELP.

'Scotty's at the jail now,' I was told.

Won't be long now, I thought, smiling at Granma over on the Monopoly board. An hour and a quarter later, just as I was happy to read in the prison manual that sex between inmates wasn't allowed, the guard called, 'Medication!'

Must be the pills to smother the libidos of these sex-fiends, I thought. But the truth was the most excited these boys got was when Lee Trevino birdied at the 7th about a half hour later.

Near twelve I called Scotty again. He was still down at the jail trying to get us out. 'Should be any minute soon,' the lady told me.

119

At noon the guard called, 'D Block! Lunch! Line up!'

I lined up with the others. Buster and Paul had lost their appetites somewhere. They went to their bunks.

Once out of D Block, we were marched down another warren of corridors to the mess hall to join about a hundred prisoners.

They had an interesting fixed menu: lasagne, carrots, grits and a glass of soda. To be eaten with a spoon. Once finished with the slop, we were stood up against the wall and given a body search in case we had stolen the spoon and had plans to stab the cook. By the tone of conversations overheard during lunch between the black prisoners, getting arrested in Florida was easier than taking a leak.

But nothing happened; no riot, no fight or shoot-out with the guards. No bullying, threats or stabbings. The most brutal assault was to the palate with the grits/lasagne combo.

We were marched back to the cells, past the grass recreation area with the free weights. This is what I hoped we'd do in the afternoon. Some low-impact aerobics, some press-ups, some curls, perhaps a friendly game of hoop, or make number plates – anything was better than watching golf.

Back in D Block, the boys got a card game going and the only black gentleman in our block kept himself amused by getting changed all afternoon. For lunch he had dressed for the occasion: he wore his orange jump-suit. But back in D Block he went straight up to his cell, took off his suit, folded it, put it on his bunk and came down in T-shirt, shorts and white tube socks. Five minutes later he got up from the table, went up to his cell, put on his jumpsuit and shower slippers and came down again. Five minutes after that he went back up again, and undressed. This went on for about an hour before the guard shouted for us. It was time to leave this menagerie.

120

We said goodbye to Karl and the transvestites. I gave my soap and toothbrush to one of the inmates who asked me for it, and we were marched back to see Mr Williams.

Mr Williams gave us back our clothes in brown bags. Only they weren't all there. Paul's leather was missing. He did not notice this until the gate had opened and we had walked out into the sunlight.

'Oh yes!' Mr Williams said when we went back and questioned him about this. 'I put it to one side for safe keeping.'

Of course. And the money missing from my wallet, too.

'What money?' said Mr Williams. 'Says here you got nothing in your wallet. Where's your receipt?'

'You didn't give me one.'

Mr Williams shrugged. 'You'll have to go talk to them across the way.' Then he turned off the intercom which was his way of saying beat it.

We were let out to meet our patron Scotty, the bondsman, a nice guy who had been at the jail now for the last five hours. With his help we got my money back, he took us to *Bob's Auto*, we fired up the d'Elegance and fled from Florida as fast as we could legally go.

Just after we made it across the state line, Buster reached into his jacket pocket and pulled out a small glassine bag.

'Anybody want to roll a joint?' he said. Somehow they hadn't found it in his coat. But even with a bone to smoke, all that money wasted was too terrible to contemplate. I did not have a pleasant ride back to New York City.

Five

Safe back in New York City, the watch and everything else worth more than a couple of nickels was taken straight down to the 23rd Street pawn. In the days that followed I could not avoid considering my current financial situation. Ruinous, that was the only word for it. The phone had been disconnected. I owed six hundred to Buster's friend for the bond, which I felt obliged to return; an additional three hundred for a Daytona lawyer called Nixon (chosen by the right sort of associations) to get the charges dropped, whose services the boys had already engaged. On top of that there was the rent and cat food.

Then one night I was on my way home from a bar after going out for a night with some new people in town, people I'd met down in the Caribbean on the boats, when I was overcome by a terrible urge to eat a hot dog. At four in the morning this is a hard thing to accomplish. Avenue C and 7th, my co-ordinates at the time, was no place to buy anything but dope.

I went over to Tompkins Square, then headed up the empty streets of the East Side, past the coloured lights of the delis, and headed for 14th Street and the Palladium. I was sure I would find a dog merchant outside the Palladium.

But there wasn't one. I walked cross town to Nell's. No merchant there, either. I went up to MK – nothing, just the bouncers, doormen, and a crowd waiting at the other side of the barrier. This was very strange. I went off to the Korean and bought a can. Then I went home and skipped into the kitchen hoping for some scraps; but the fridge was empty. Then I had a blinding inspiration. Just before falling over the mattress that night, I said to the cat: there's a business opportunity here, in hot dogs. And free food for you and me. I will think about this.

And I must have done a lot of it in my sleep because when I woke in the morning to a car alarm in the parking lot opposite, my head was filled with great ideas. Packing toothbrushes for a living – the current job – was not properly utilizing my natural abilities, I said to myself. Even for a man like me with such clearly unpronounced natural abilities. Entrepreneurism – now this is what I should be trying, to improve my daily lot.

I dressed and hurried out of the house to work, full of conviction.

That day, as I put one brush in front of the next, made one box after the next, a clear, romantic vision fixed itself in my noodle. My first real business enterprise. A hot dog empire. I would have the smartest hot dog cart in the city, one with lights, horns and flags and long lines of the drunk and hungry clamouring for my product. I would have money in my pocket and that was just for starters. Ideas like this can make dynasties.

Skating home from work that night I started to consider names for this enterprise, but after a minute of it I had to quit. Names are not easy; especially the sort that drive themselves into the deepest recesses of the human experience. I needed something Pavlovian; something the mere suggestion of which would make you snort and paw the earth. I needed something to bring out the dog in man.

It just so happened that as I came down 5th Avenue on my board, untouched by the Muse, on my way to a

123

rendezvous with a can, a little distracted by the need to find a name, I ran smack into a girl.

She was one of the prettiest girls I had knocked over in a long time: red-painted nails, a dark, brown, double-breasted fitted jacket, silver hoops in her ears, hair and eyes as black as onyx, a fitted short skirt and a beautiful, delicate face that was now red with rage.

Naturally, this young lady was ready to tear my eyes out; but that was all right. It was a pleasure to be yelled at by someone so pretty. And as she was bawling and cussing and telling me how close I had come to killing her, watched by an old crazy man who kept saying, 'Tell him as it is, sister! Sho' you're right! Sho' you're right! Smack him upside da head! Smack him upside da head!', from right out of nowhere came the name for my first attempt at running my own business.

'Big Dick's Hot Dog Company,' I said out loud.

As I said the name over and over, I thought perhaps I was just having another smutty thought – I was having a lot of them at the time and this girl was gorgeous – but by the time I had stopped grinning, and finally apologized to the girl and helped her on her way, I thought this name was exactly what I was looking for and very befitting to my customer, if I was going to cater to the night crowd. I would sell the sexiest dog in the business, on the smartest cart. Big Dick's Hot Dog Co! You'll never believe how big it is! Something snappy like that.

I got back on my board and rode down the hill to the Korean to get myself a can. Then I went home. And as I headed up the three flights of bare stairs to the loft I realized that this great opportunity for wealth had come to me exactly a week before we were scheduled to throw a party. This party was special. Guests would pay five dollars on the door and pay to drink, but since the bar didn't have a licence the whole caboodle was illegal.

124

My role was the booze. Six hundred customers would be right there (it was hoped), queuing up to be polite and patient. Why not, I thought, take the opportunity to sell 'em a plump and delicious Big Dick's tasty dog? Big, the way you like 'em, madam. Yo ho.

Only reason I could think of was money. I was in no position to fund the enterprise and for a brief moment was unable to think of any capital streams to tap (no bank account, nothing left to hock). Then I remembered I had a rich roommate.

Pedro ate regularly (and in restaurants – real ones, not coffee houses, diners, or kebab trolleys), paid his rent on time, bought clothes from Union in Soho, came home with an armful of new records at least once or twice a week, and was, by comparison, rolling in it.

That night, as he was bent over the gas burners fixing his tortilla and beans, I got braced to give him the pitch. With him it was imperative not to distract his attention near the feeding hours. He loved his food; any interruption during the preparation of his daily feast would either damage chances significantly or fall on deaf ears. I waited until the boys (the newsman was home early that night with his Sapporo and his history books) were at the table in front of their steaming tortillas before I brought it up.

I told Pedro everything – from the time I came home from the bar to the name that had come to me by divine collision.

'Think about it,' I said. 'What do you want most when you come out a night-club?'

'A cab.'

This is what I meant by being loaded.

'No, no, no,' I told him. 'That's not what you want. A big hot dog – that is what you want at three in the morning.'

His face was blank. But I was not about to give up. The

rest of the evening I worked on him explaining the huge potential this hot dog company offered us. In my eyes this business would make us rich men. It would give Pedro a green card and tables at the finest restaurants in the city. And all he had to put in was a hundred dollars, which is what he'd pay for a dinner with some friends over at Peter Luger's Steakhouse in Williamsburg.

In the end he agreed to make a small investment, probably because he wanted some peace, not because he shared the same tumescent vision as me. But he would. My faith could have built Disney castles out of mud. It would just take a while with him.

Dreams of loot and trucks visited me for the first time ever as I slept that night with the cat. It was a good night's sleep.

The following day was a Saturday. When my friend finally rose around lunchtime I told him we had business to attend to. We needed to get with it. He yawned and disappeared into the bathroom with a copy of Iron Horse for the next hour and a half. By around four he was ready to take a stroll down to the West Village.

The wholesale meatmarket on 14th was for the professional poor. No diet sodas, no lite food, no already-washed salad, no exotica, just meat and the basics. In the refrigerated meat department slaughtered pigs, skinned and hooked, hung on rails, ready to be loaded into shopping carts by fat women; packets of different cuts of meat filled long racks. It was Fort Knox for a man in the meat trade. I dragged Pedro straight to the back.

There we found our future, vacu-packed. *Nathans Bigger Than The Bun Skinless Beef Franks* – eight wieners, $2.78. And that was just one of many brands.

Being new to the game did not mean we were fools. We made comparisons: *Taystees U-Pay $1.59 for 8*? Or, *Arnolds* (with flavoured bread crumbs, or with plain bread

126

crumbs) eight for $2.39? *Oscar Mayer, America's Favourite Wiener* $2.78 for ten? Or, *Kosher Dogs* with strict rabbinical supervision by the good Rabbi C. Katz of Passaic . . . and so on.

Half an hour later we had made our selection and had our first partners' disagreement.

'Probably ought to buy a thousand,' I said.

'Be lucky if we sell a hundred,' said my partner.

As he was paying I could not say anything more.

That night, at the loft, we had a testing. The dog we chose did not disappoint. With its high levels of sodium and flavouring it made us thirsty. The bar would profit. But first we had to commission a billboard for the advertising.

Pedro said he knew just the right person – the right person was any person who would do the work in exchange for a night of free drink. Pedro's friend was an artist student who lived in Greenwich Village and was known to his friends as Homeless.

We went to see this Homeless the following day. 'What we need is something tasteful and subtle, you know,' said my partner to the young man as we stood in the rubble of a front room of an apartment down at Waverly Place.

'No, no, no,' I said. 'What we want is sex! This is a sexy hot dog. You understand that, Homeless? Make it sexy and we're in the money.'

The artist wasn't listening. He was putting the finishing work to a large conical joint. I told him again. He said he'd have something for us in a few days.

A few days passed. Then a few more. I called but the phone was never answered. Finally, on the Saturday, a week later, the day of the event, we found our artist. He had been visiting in Brooklyn for the week, he said.

'What about the great work?' I asked. 'How is it shaping up? Is it, you know, finished?'

'No.'

127

'No? Well, is it, hmmm, coming along okay?'

'Not really.'

'What does not really mean?'

'It isn't started,' said the artist nonchalantly.

'Not started? We open tonight! How are we going to do any business if the people don't know what we're selling, for Chrissakes?'

'Don't worry, man,' the artist said to console me. 'The work will be finished by – ' He yawned loudly. 'Opening. I'll bring it to you.'

I had other matters to worry about. The place we had chosen for the night was down in the Lower East Side on Rivington Street: a wildlife reserve for pipe-heads, alcoholics, and nickel bag heroin dealers. To get the place ready for the night's fête would require cunning. A low profile was needed to sneak the fifty crates of booze and the stadium-sized PA sound system into the place. If we didn't, once the local residents knew that this was going to be a party, there was no guarantee they wouldn't barge through the door with their semi-automatics and hold the place up. Maintaining secrecy was the key to keeping the cash, avoiding being shot, and staying out of trouble. But by the time the booze was unloaded from a van at four that afternoon, the whole neighbourhood knew about it.

At seven o'clock that night, just as the two trestle-tabled bars were being set up on the stage of the old theatre, we had a visit from the police of the local precinct. There was a burglary in progress next door, they said (there's always a burglary in progress next door somewhere on this street). Had we happened to see any felons running through here in the last ten minutes?

We hadn't.

Did we mind, then, they asked, if they came up the stairs to take a look around? Just in case the felons had broken

128

into the building and were hiding somewhere without our knowledge? You know, just in case?

At the top of the stairs (we stood at street-level, by the triple titanium reinforced, neighbour-resistant, cast-iron swing-doors) there were thirty cases of beer, assorted cases of hard liquor, a table, a chair, people putting up signs like 'GROOVE' and 'LOVE', a book of entry tickets and a cash till. Since this was illegal – having no permit or insurance – letting these men in was a risk. But we had no choice; not letting them in would be much too suspicious.

Once up in the main ballroom area, the two officers made a number of interesting observations. We had quite some sound system. It was a good place to throw a party. And – what a well-stocked bar we had!

So, they asked, what's the event?

'A surprise birthday party,' all smiles.

Judging by their smiles they didn't give two shakes either way. We offered them drink, free entry and introductions to all the ladies we knew if they cared to come back later. They said they might. After a walk around the dance floor, stage area and back stairs, they left.

Just before nine, the artist showed up with his work, looking pleased with himself. With a cup of vodka to help him with his presentation, he opened up his combat jacket to show me the great work.

'It's good, no?' he said, lighting a joint.

It was very fine but what he had given me was something drawn on the flap of a cardboard box. What I needed was something big and informative like a billboard. When I asked him about the size of it he said that he could not afford paper and we were not paying for it, so a flap was all we were getting, puff, puff, puff.

Never mind, said Pedro, who was having problems keeping a straight face. What a magnificent flap, heh? Just look at it. Just look at the whole eight inches of it. Besides

129

– who cares about the flap as long as there's lots of pretty girls to chase.

Pedro was having difficulty making the necessary adjustments to becoming a businessman.

With everything for the night now set, we caught a cab uptown to the loft (we wrote it off on the business) and an hour later we were back at Rivington Street with the dogs, whilst the newsman started to spin some of his records. We installed the dogs behind the bar in a large casserole dish. This and a kitchen kettle full of water was Pedro's fine idea for saving money (a hot-dog cart cost too much to rent). The condiments were set up to one side, with the buns, next to the sign; then we fixed ourselves some drinks and settled down to wait.

At ten o'clock, the security hired for the evening opened the doors. Nobody arrived for the first hour and a half. Once they did though, my business partner, all dressed up in his finery, sporting a new pair of bell-bottoms, chest-hair, and a gold whistle on a chain with fake precious stones on it, decided hot dogs weren't for him, but a girl called Lizzie was. He abandoned his post as soon as he caught sight of her coming through the door in a sequinned dress.

'I'll be back in a minute,' he said. That was the last I saw of him for the night.

Two hours into the evening the place was packed. Only problem was I didn't sell anything. Nobody seemed to be much interested in buying one of my plump and delicious dogs. Big, the way you, etc. Another thing. Since it was so loud and dark, the customers couldn't see my sign, nor my great product, nor understand what I was yelling. I grabbed a handful of pretty girls and asked them to stand behind the bar and eat as much as they could, with as much pleasure on their faces as possible and I wouldn't charge them a cent.

130

'Do we have to?' they whined.

But even with their pretty faces eating my great dogs and showing oodles of pleasure nobody seemed to want to buy anything but vodka and cranberry. The girls refused to sell them topless, so next I gave some out as samples, thinking if one person was seen with a dog another person would want one and the old floodgates would be thrown open. They weren't. Something was afoot. Instead of stuffing themselves with my dogs, the crowd seemed much too interested in dancing, kissing, and fondling each other. This was not in the business plan. It was long after evening meals had been consumed and by my estimation, high time these drunkards should have been queuing up. But they weren't. Kiss, schmooze, peck, peck . . . Darling, how are you? Vodka, cranberry? Blah, blah, blah, but no hot dog.

I ate a few whilst I poured the cups for the mob and moaned. Such fine dogs! But nobody cared. Not long after I discovered what the problem was: a fat dope-dealer with blond dreads, a sequin jacket with big red stars all over it, eighteen-hole silver DMs and a tin lunch-box full of powerful drugs. He stole all my business. All I heard from the crowd from around one-thirty onwards was general bragging of who had taken what drug and how warm, loving and affectionate it made them feel. This man got the house so looped nobody wanted to eat. And the organizers were the worst offenders of all. After two o'clock, there was no one on the door to take entrance money and nobody coming around the bars to take the large cash floats from bar sales; they were all on the dance-floor somewhere schmoozing. Even the DJ was off his face. Near 3 a.m. he shut down the music and shouted over the PA, '*Check . . . this . . . out!*'

We did. Nothing much happened.

'*I'm gonna fuck with your minds . . .*'

Might have been the plan but he got too confused by

131

everything, forgot what great record he was going to use to accomplish this great feat and blew all the fuses in the house. The replacement DJ stepped in and the other lurched out from behind the tables and stood, wide-eyed and dripping with sweat, gazing at the hundreds and thousands of little mirrors on the ball suspended from above. For the next ten minutes he stood under this shiny ball, sweating and gnawing his top lip until it ballooned and filled half his face.

I quit. At three-thirty that morning Big Dick's Hot Dog Co. closed. We had sold the unimpressive sum of twelve hot dogs. But in the wake of this commercial disaster, a few good things were to come. We weren't held up; I had made some good money on the bar; and a nice painter asked me if I wanted to take her home to give her a spanking.

And that wasn't all. The lady Pedro had chased all night worked in nightclubs. She told me that she loved me so much she would get me a real job, at a real club, where the organizers were straight and the job regular. I went down the club to meet the owner, was offered a job, and thus left the hot dog and toothbrush-packing businesses for the more exotic, secure and exciting world of the nightclubs of Manhattan. What a mistake.

Six

Months later, near midnight, on a Thursday, at the night-club where I had been working full time, my head was up against the chest of a young girl, my ear was between her sharp teeth, and when she wasn't chewing it, she was trying to tell me about doing something called the wild thing, or the nasty.

'The what?'

'Would you like to have sex with us?' said the girl, who was probably no older than sixteen.

She stroked my face. What she had said had thrown me and I had to take a step back from the bar and shake. Three months earlier I would have jumped all over an offer like this; but these days I couldn't, even if I had wanted to and I didn't anymore. Not unless I was absolutely sure of a number of things, but that would have been impossible because I was not sure of anything anymore – except this: I had a whooping cough, fevers twice a day, sleepless nights and a hangover that had lasted about two months. I kept thinking something better was going to come my way before things really got out of shape; but it hadn't and I didn't know if it would. After four months of work in a nightclub I had started to believe all sorts of fool things; the worst of which was that this life was normal, better than most, paid me more money than I'd ever felt in my pocket, and certainly, in a warped fashion, was interesting.

In the first month I was there, when I thought I'd fallen

on my feet and walked into a job I'd like to keep for a long, long time, I became smitten by a girl I'd seen in the club as a dancer. She was beautiful. A big-boned blonde. She danced on the go-go box in front of where I worked. I would send her drinks. Every night I went home thinking about her. A couple of weeks later I asked her out. We had a night and at the end of it, just as I was about to put my lips on hers, she told me she was an hermaphrodite.

'I've still got my organs,' she said proudly. 'You wanna see?'

When I told the other bartenders at work the next day they said I shouldn't worry about it, what the hell, you know she's going to know what to do better than any woman anyway. And for a while I was tempted and curious; but then I started to notice hands too big, fingers too fat, feet too large, shoulders too wide, a voice deeper than my own, and silicone-implanted breasts that did not move when she danced. I don't know why I hadn't noticed it before, but I hadn't and this confused me.

Everything confused me, and that was why I was taken aback by the offer from the girls standing in front of me at my bar. I'd never met them before. I'd never even seen them before, but within two minutes of coming to the bar they had asked me if I wanted to do this wild thing.

'So, how 'bout it?' one of them asked.

I started coughing.

'Nice club,' she said when I didn't answer her.

'That's what you think.'

'Whad'ya mean?'

On this particular evening, I told her, there were more men wearing dresses than women; and some of these men wore nothing but pantyhose, feather boas, and scooted around the dancefloor on rollerskates. How about that for a nice club?

'Wow. That's sort of cool,' said the girl, giggling.

So then I told her this: earlier that evening, just after I had arrived at the club, I heard the manager, Liz, ask the drag-queen, Chucky, how to become more ladylike. How about that?

'That's funny.'

'What's your name?' I asked.

'Katey,' she said. Then she grabbed me by the back of the neck and put her tongue in my ear. 'Have you ever been to bed with two women?' she shouted.

'I can't remember.'

'It's natural!' said Katey.

'That's right,' said the other. 'That's why there are *two* times as many women as men!'

So, God had something to do with it, then. I asked her if that was what she meant. She nodded.

'Exactly!' the girl said. 'Now kiss me!'

I leant over the bar to peck her on the cheek, but that wasn't good enough for her. She wanted tongue.

'Can't do it,' I said.

'Don't you like us?'

'Nothing to do with it,' I told them.

'Aren't you feeling all right?'

'As a matter of fact, I've never felt worse.'

I smiled, made a drink for myself, lit a cigarette and started one of the loudest coughing jags of the night so far.

The girl pointed her finger at me. 'You,' she said, 'are wacko.'

'You haven't met Bouncer Stevie,' I said when I could get the words out.

'Bouncer who?'

'Bouncer Stevie.'

I told her Bouncer Stevie wore four-hundred-dollar Italian loafer driving shoes to work at night, tight jeans, a T-shirt, and his work was to crack skulls. Now if it had

135

been me doing his job I'd have worn boots with razors around the toes, a flak jacket and packed a .357 shooter.

'Wacko,' said Katey.

'Fruity,' said her friend. 'But he'll do. Say, you gonna give a girl a drink?'

'What sort of drink?'

'Sex-on-the-beach.'

I started mixing a drink, a sex-on-the-beach. I said, 'A night working Hip-Hop here is like a night at Khe-Sanh. You ever been to Khe-Sanh?'

'No,' the girl said. 'Where's that?'

'Never mind.'

I told these girls that with a couple of sex-on-the-beaches down their pants, the kids in this club went bananas. Just two weeks earlier an Hispanic was pistol-whipped in the men's room and carted off in an ambulance with a forehead the size of a ripe watermelon. Same night three kids got jumped and stabbed outside on the street. Next night a fight blew up on the dance-floor and a gang chased one kid over to the coat-check area, clubbed him over the head with a Dom Perignon champagne bucket, slammed his fingers in the coat-check door, then beat him until he was unconscious. The following day the victim rang up the club to say what a fine old time he'd had the night before but was wondering, did anybody hand in his jewellery? And that was the reason he had kicked his sorry self all over the dance floor.

'Bouncer Stevie has to deal with this shit every night, in driving shoes and a tight T-shirt,' I said. 'Does that sound like the actions of a sane man to you?'

The girl shrugged and smiled. 'Are you going to give us some more free drinks, or what?'

I mixed them sex-on-the-beaches. Then, feeling a little looser, I asked them, for the sake of continuing conversation, if they happened to know that Ken Doll, aka Action

Man – the plastic toy soldier I played battle with in the front room, the doll I was given each time my mother had a son, a pretty fine toy in other words, one of the very best – had a pretty fucking exuberant sense of how to let his short hair down when he wasn't busy fighting for freedom and democracy.

'Oh,' the one girl said, after chugging half the cup. 'What d'you mean by that?'

I told her there were slides projected above the dance floor, right on the far wall if she cared to turn around and take a look, which showed that what Ken really liked to do when kids like me were asleep was to skip out of Toy Box Central Command on his R & R and make for Christopher Street to get his nose and nipples pierced, trade battle fatigues for drag, snort poppers, and go to gay orgies at the Ramrod for a session with the whips.

'That's funny!' the girl said, but I didn't think so. It was upsetting. I asked her if she knew Barbie Doll.

The girl nodded.

'Barbie Doll is a cocaine addict,' I told her.

'A what?' said the girl who was starting to look at me in a peculiar manner.

'A junkie.'

I told her I had seen photographic evidence of Barbie slide-projected onto the wall above the crowds, same spot as Ken, sitting naked on a pink satin sheet with a lipstick-smeared face and mussed hair, looking like she had just come down after a six-day screamer with the white powder.

'Barbie Doll was fucked up?' the girl asked me.

'That's right. She had a sign around her neck which said, '*I'm addicted to Cocaine*''.

'No way!'

'If you ask me there's more sanity in Bellevue than in this joint. A lot more. Here, have a cigarette, but light the filter, all right? That's the way we do it in here.'

Shortly after this the girls left. I started coughing until the tears ran down my face.

A while later, I was looking out onto the crowded dance-floor, sort of numb about everything, and I saw a girl dancing with an older leather queen. She followed him around the dance-floor trying to turn him, whilst he made eyes at a skinny, tall, black kid with a whistle round his neck, a peaked cap and his summer Gap clothes. This girl must have been some kind of egomaniac because she wouldn't take no for an answer.

'Do you like me?' I heard the girl ask.

'Sure.'

'No, I mean do you really like me?'

The man shrugged, waggled his butt, and smoked. 'I like men,' he said.

She stroked his face and then whispered in his ear, 'But I'll bet you've never slept with a woman like me before!'

The man wagged his index finger in front of her face. 'You're nice. But what you got, honey, I don't want. And what I got . . .' Waggle, waggle, waggle. '. . . you ain't gonna get.' Then he danced off.

I turned my attentions back to the bar. Some hoodlums were waiting to be served.

'Yo! Bartender! Yo! Gimme Kamikaze.'

The thing about these boys is they don't know manners, but are experts at demanding your attention.

'Yo! Fix me a Long Island,' one shouted at me. Then the whole pack of them started braying like wild dogs: 'Yo! Five sex-on-the-beach. Yo gimme yo bartender yo motherfucker a drink yo . . .'

Which normally made me feel like leaning across the counter and punching a couple of lights out; but assaulting the customers was not allowed. Management had a note by the ice bunker and time-clock which read: *To all employees, if any bartender gets involved in future altercations with*

138

the customers – you'll all be fired! The Management. This was the owner's way of communicating with the staff. Besides, it wasn't worth taking the chance to smack 'em. Although the frisking policy at the door was good, these kids broke the guns down into parts and their girlfriends smuggled them into the club in their pocket-books. The guns were then assembled in the men's room and the kids strolled through the club ready to shoot bartenders or anybody else who happened to piss them off. And some of them were no more than seventeen.

'Yo! I'm talkin' to you. Fix me sum'p'n to get me *fucked up.*'

One of them was leaning over my bar, looking for something to steal. I threw a plastic cup at him.

'Can't do it,' I said.

'Why? Ain't you da man round here?'

'That really all depends.'

'Depenz on what?' he asked.

'Depends on if I fucking feel like it.'

He laughed. 'Yo – so what if we wuz to tip you?'

'How much?'

The one with a pig's hoop in his nose, grinned. 'Gi' you a quarter.'

'Nope,' I said.

'A dollar, then,' he said.

'Two.'

'Yo – why two fucking dollars?'

'All right, three.'

'Suppose I ain't gonna pay you no three fucking dollars?'

'You ain't gonna get no fucking drink.'

He gave me the eye but fuck the little fuck. Since these boys constantly heckled for more booze, less ice, faster service, lower prices, and rarely left me a nickel, I always said, if they wanted a free drink, there was plenty of water in the men's room, and if the sinks were busy there was always the toilet bowl, if they didn't mind getting their big heads wet. They walked off, cursing.

Emile, the Polish night manager, was next up to the bar. Emile had a pony-tail and always dressed in black. It was his firm belief he could tell in under ten seconds which girl would go to bed with him and how long it would take. This occupied most of his thinking at night. He wanted to know how business was.

'Fine.'

I fixed him a Bacardi and coke, two limes, and he went off to check the clickers at the entrance and exit. The clickers were to fool the Fire Department if they were to come into the club at night to make a check to see if there were more than the four-hundred-and-seventy-three people allowed in.

By now it was near one. The house music was turned down and a spotlight shone onto the balcony above my bar. I moved around the side to take a look.

Sister Dimension, the drag-queen of world-famous repu-tation and beauty, walked out into the light. The Sister was the host for the evening and wore a red party dress, red high-heels, rhinestone sun-glasses, a lacquered perox-ide wig, false eyelashes shaped like ski-jumps and raw glitter on his ghost-white cheeks.

'Welcome all you fabulous people!' the Sister said. 'Welcome to Panty-Girdles! Thank you. Tonight, tonight as most of you know, we're having an AIDS fund-raiser. Yes! An auction of *Sex Slaves*!'

How terrific. The crowd on the floor hooted and whistled. I started coughing until a nice, big lump came up in my throat which I spat out.

'Ladies and gentlemen, boys and girls, I want you all to give a big hand for our first slave of the night, the *fierrrrce Sweeeeetyyy*!'

140

A light-skinned fifteen-year-old Hispanic kid strutted out onto the lit balcony like a catwalk model.

'Everybody! Everybody – put your hands together!' the Sister said. 'Oh, that's so much better! Now bitch, take that shirt off! Uh-huh. Take it offfff! Show the fabulous people what you got.'

The shirt came off. Some of the boys in the audience thought Sweety was quite some piece. Sweety paraded around the balcony smiling at the crowd, playing with his muscles.

The Sister stamped his foot. 'Hello! Hello! Do I hear one dollar?'

Someone offered a dollar. Sweety smiled and blew a few kisses.

'Do I hear babadabadabadaba *three* dollars for this fierce-fabulous young man? Make it a dollar and a quarter and go home and give me some peace. Sweety could buy a subway token.'

Someone offered three dollars.

'Okay. Now, bitch, show us some buns!'

Anthony Magnifique, Aldawna, Geraldo, Rodney Xtravaganza, and the members of Dee-Lite – who had gathered in the wings away from the spotlight – all cheered and laughed when Sweety dropped his pants. The Sister stroked Sweety's buttocks. I started coughing again.

'Now, do I hear five dollars for this hot, sexy, hunky, young male?' the Sister asked.

He got the five and the bidding got as high as seventeen. Then Sister demanded twenty-five. Nobody wanted to pay the twenty-five. Sweety retired from the stage waving and blowing kisses.

Four more of these sex-slaves came out with varying degrees of success, but the money offered wasn't much. Not considering all the hoopla. The Sister needed something to get the crowd going.

141

Sister brought out the pop star, Lady Miss Kier Kirby, the girl from Dee-Lite. She was very fine looking. Someone ended up bidding about a hundred for her. I believe it was her husband. Next up were some men introduced as Jo-Jo and his Jock Straps.

'They're gorgeous!' said the Sister. 'Well hung! Uncut! New York's next singing sensations!'

Black plastic PVC bondage clothes, dreadlocks, thigh-high black plastic boots might be the rage in some fashion circles but it didn't do an awful lot for me. The bidding made fifty dollars.

Fake money started falling from the ceiling. 'C'mon, kids!' said the Sister. 'Cash up the bucket! Yeah! This is the stuff *dreeeeeams* are made of!'

I had another coughing fit and another drink. A big one. Madonna's *Vogue* pumped out the speakers. The Sister started to vogue. A couple of gay Hispanic kids read each other on the floor, with a circle of people watching them.

'And now people,' the Sister said. 'And now people we have a very special attraction for you this evening. Salt . . .'N' . . . Pe*ppa*! Two *hot* secretaries from the World Trade Center! Come out here girls, c'mon!'

The girls came vogueing into the spotlight and they were gorgeous. I was sort of tempted to put in a bid, but likely as not they were probably men anyway and that would be throwing money up the wall. One was black, one white.

'Okay, okay, okay – now people, people, do I hear a hundred dollars?' the Sister asked.

He did. The bids soared. I watched the Sister coax the crowd and I was sure I had a sense of déjà vu. Then I knew it: Vanna White. Offering a new prize on *Wheel of Forrrtunnne*. My, my, my. I finished one drink and fixed another. The bidding went to three hundred.

Others came out, were bid for – some made money, some didn't – and when there weren't any more slaves to be sold off, Sweety, the first of these slaves to have come out for auction, decided his bag of bones was worth more than the paltry seventeen bucks someone had bid for him, so he came out again with a young man who was as bald as a coot and wore blue sequin shorts cut like a 1930s swimsuit.

The Sister got the bids going, but they weren't much, thirty dollars. Sweety wanted more. He took the microphone and shouted: 'I'll be sure to put out! Dinner, sex – *evvverthing*!!!'

And loopy bastard meant it too. The queens on the balcony howled. I fixed another drink, but the price didn't rise much. So Sweety stripped off his shirt, pulled down his pants, put his hand down his black lurex jocks and masturbated. This got him another five dollars.

I was glad to hear Bouncer Stevie cry, 'Take her to hotel, motel – any place. But get her the fuckouddah here! We're *closed*!' not so long after. After pooling the tips and saying goodnight to everyone, I went home. I was ready for my post at the TV.

But at quarter-to-five in the morning there is not much on TV. All I could find was the *Richard Simmonds Deal-A-Meal Show*; or, *How To Get Rich Through Real Estate*; or endless re-runs of *Amazing Discoveries*; or *1-900 Reward*; or Jessica Hahn and her *Love Phone*. So I switched the TV off. I turned out the lights, climbed the loft stairs and lay on my mattress in the dark listening to the car alarm in the lot opposite, and waited a long time to get off to sleep. I started laughing for no reason at all. I turned on my bedside lamp and took out some of Carla's letters from the tin by my bed. I tried to read the ones where she was telling me about the new kid she was expecting and the new home they were hoping to move into: no good. I threw them to one side and took out the pictures of the Spanish girl that Ram had drawn for me all those years ago.

Couldn't see her either. I tried to sleep again. The following day would be Friday. I never looked forward to working Fridays.

Friday was the worst night of the week. DJ Slave spun. Slave was a one man penal system. He played Alternative Music. Slave's Alternative Music was a misnomer – what he played was an alternative to music. And he played it on Alternative Night, every Friday, which filled the club with Alternative People who had Alternative ideas about everything. They liked black T-shirts with slogans like *You Deserve To Go To Hell*. Or, *Blow Me, Then Leave*. Or, *Jesus Christ Proudly Presents: Christian Death*. They wore patchouli oil and slamdanced. Alternatives lived in Alternative Places like New Jersey, ate Alternative Food and had Alternative Jobs which meant they were still in high school. That's not to say they were not nice. They were the salt of the earth, but no good for a bartender because they had no money. I never made a dime out of them and always came home with a headache.

On this particular Friday, Jack, the Polish busboy, let me in. He was taking the bars off the doors at the time I walked up; but he was unhappy. His car had been vandalised. It was an old General Motors, with Old Glory waving on the antenna. He asked me what he should do.

'Go live somewhere else.'

We went inside, out of the heat, where it was cold, dark, and air-conditioned. We went down the stairs to the dancefloor at basement level. I said hello to everybody. I went to punch in. Then I noticed a stage had been set up with a drum kit, mike stands, and big banks of speakers. This was bad news. There was going to be a performance of Alternative Music. This is worse than hearing the stuff on record.

I started to set up my bar at a spot called Dance Floor North. DJ Slave walked past with his bandana and portable torture chamber: a milk crate of Alternative records.

'See you in Kiev,' he said.

The 24-hour coffee shop and restaurant, Kiev, down on 8th Street, is where we all went to eat breakfast when the club closed – if we didn't go to an after-hours joint, or go home to watch Jessica Hahn.

'Slave, where do you live?' I asked.

'Long Island, man,' he said.

'So tell me – why didn't you stay there, no offence?'

'Because I love music, man. I'm a slave to music.'

'I like music too. But a night of listening to your stuff – if there was a choice of that or being mugged, I'd take being mugged.'

Slave was definitely insulted.

'Man, that was cold,' said Sabina, one of the nicest, and the prettiest bartender in the place. She was standing next to me cutting limes for the night.

I cut my limes. On Fridays you didn't have to cut so many because nobody had any money to buy cocktails. I put out the bev naps, took the plastic cups off the booze in the speed racks, put the drink straws in a glass, laid the bar mat on the bar, and fixed a large drink for me and for Sabina.

Soon the music started. No one came to the bar to buy drinks but some people started dancing to a tune called *Gossip – The House of Blood*.

A while later the first person came to my bar. He wanted a free drink, everybody does, but he killed his chances when he said, 'I'm with the band.' I told him to go see Emile and cop some comp tickets.

The next up wasn't much better.

'If I get a coupla drinks, do I get buy-backs?' the kid – he probably wasn't even eighteen – asked.

'Nope.'

'You fucking blow.'

145

He ran from the bar before I could wing some ice at him.

At midnight it got better. Primitec, the three piece, came on. These boys had an interesting look – both singers wore diapers and war paint. The back-up singer had a plastic band around his waist with 'CAUTION' written on it. I think he stole it from a road-site. Behind them there was a lady in rags smacking a drum and hopping up and down on one foot as if she was dancing on a bed of hot coals. I stopped fixing drinks for myself to pay attention.

'Good evening everyone,' said the lead singer in a swirl of rancid smoke. 'My name is Atom. I'm your emcee squared!'

Atom had a haircut on him inspired by elementary geometry textbooks. His hair patterns were triangles: isosceles on his chin, right angles on his cheeks, and an equilateral arrangement up on top. He said, 'Yes! Evening Seed Men! Nude Women! *P-rimitive* Men! My mother has *melted*! I have ultra-violet fear bouncing off my painted body! A pop landscape of ghosts with Wendy's Hot'N'Juicy and Weenies That Won The West . . .'

The girl in rags who was dancing in the background let out a shriek and flopped on the stage.

'On and on into the toxic hole! Flapping and snapping and snapping and flapping into the solar windpipe mushrooming all around me looking down at the family of forefathers! B-lue mother! Red man! B-lack man! Yellow man! G-reen woman! Sick! Sick! *Sick*!'

I applauded and hooted loudly. This was probably the most fun we'd had in here on a Friday night for years. It almost made me feel good.

'The contaminated rivers of the Hudson!' said Atom. 'The contaminated rivers of Chernobyl! Burning tar on the feathers of fallen angels! I *do* believe in moolah! I *do* believe in moolah! I *do* believe in moolah!'

He got very excited about this idea. I did too. I was just about to hop over the bar and head off for a leak when Wayne, the Head of Security for the club, came over to fix himself a coke. Wayne is a prince, all three-hundred-and-something pounds of him.

'No real surprise that the club is closing, is it?' he said. This was news to me and I thought about this whilst listening to a kid being violently sick in the men's room.

When I got back to my bar the band had commenced the singing part of their act. This was a mistake. Up until that moment I was a fan. Toxic waste, the apocalypse, nuclear destruction, three-headed babies – I had strong emotional empathy with all these things after working with Slave. But once Atom started singing, he lost me. I sulked all the way through the performance and was hard-pressed to put my hands together when the lights went down at the end of their act and Slave started to spin more records.

'Dude – what kinda beer you got on draught?'

A curtain of crusted black hair was standing at the bar. A hand cleared the matted hair and I saw a pimpled face.

'Schlitz,' I said.

'Uuurk! *Donkey piss*! A'right, a'right – how much d'ya charge?'

'Three.'

'Dude, man, that's a rip off.'

'I don't make the prices. I just work here.'

'Fuck you, then.'

A couple of hours later, near quarter-to-three, with the place packed with spooks and ghouls, Slave put on one of the Alternatives' all time favourites: Ministry's *Thieves*. Just after the opening beat a circle formed on the dance-floor and they started slamming under the flashing strobes.

Jesse, another bartender, came running past me to go on the floor and join in. Jesse was a nut for a good slam. But

147

when it was over and everyone had beaten each other up, Jesse came back and told me he thought he must be getting a little old. Somebody had put a choke hold on him and held him until he had almost passed out. He went back to his bar, and a kid came over and asked me if his nose was broke. It was bleeding. I told him it probably was.

'*Yeah*!' he said, pleased and excited. He ran off to tell his cronies.

Some time later a punk with green ice-cream cone hair, bondage gear, and enough nose, ear, and lip rings to tag a herd of swine caught my eye. He was foraging along my bar, picking up smoked butts and empty beer cans to see if there was anything left for him to smoke or drink. When he arrived opposite me he cleared his throat and said: 'How much d'you charge for a Rock'n'Roll?'

'Four fifty.'

'You mean to tell me you charge *four dollars and fifty cents* for a twelve ounce can of shitty *Rolling Rock* beer?'

'That's right.'

'Man, if I was a cop – I'd *arrest* you!'

'And if I worked for Roaches-R-Us, you'd be terminated. Beat it.'

Just before closing, when the crowds on the floor had thinned, I overheard a conversation between two girls. The first said, 'So you've found a guy? That's great! Congratulations!'

'Don't clap too much,' the other girl said. 'He's tripping.'

We walked with seventy dollars each that night. But we had Saturday night to look forward to. Saturday meant Techno House with Jason and Marek. I went home and was sick nicely, all over the fish tank. Slave's fault. That's how I reasoned.

Work, this man Kahlil Gibran, a respected oracle of opinion, said, is love made visible. Gibran never had to work open bar in the VIP lounge on Saturday night. The bar is six deep with gnashing teeth and desperate people, all wanting to order fifty-one cocktails, all waving fists in your face, and all ready to rip your throat out if you don't serve them. These kids are on a one-hour mission to get shit-faced for free. I hated it and had a strong hunch this was Management's way of expressing their displeasure. Putting you on open bar. I was working open bar that night.

Sabina, Wendy, Pam, Cissy and Jesse were smart when they had to work in this hole: they insisted for each drink they made, they be tipped a dollar; four drinks four dollars – no tipee, no drinkee, as Taylor the barback would say. I kept meaning to put up a sign: *Show Me A Dollar And You Won't Have To Holler* but didn't. I probably served six-hundred mixed drinks, two-hundred cans of Rolling Rock, and made only two-hundred-and-twenty-five dollars in two hours that night (some of the girls made three, four-hundred during open bar).

'Tsk!' said Sabina when she came up to my bar around 1.30 to find out how I had done. 'You're a sorry ass motherfucker!'

I shrugged and coughed.

'Are you all right? You look kinda ill.'

Sabina offered to take my bar for a while in consideration of my poor condition. I crept out the hatch at the back and made my way through the crowd into the heat and the noise. The dwarf from Twin Peaks was at the top of the stairs of the VIP room, next to a big black man with no shirt and an eight-foot boa constrictor wound around his neck. I went down the stairs. I passed a man with feathers on his crotch, a painted red body and two little horns on his head, holding a vodka and cranberry.

A promoter, one of the kids paid to hand out invites for one club in other clubs, handed me a card. I read:

149

10's . . . 10's . . . 10's . . . 10's . . . 10's . . . 10's . . . 10's!

Across the board!!

THE
HOUSE OF
XTRAVAGANZA

You have seen us in the movie Paris Is Burning.
You have seen us on Donahue and Geraldo.
Now see us live! On stage at the
LIMELIGHT

We're not going to be shady . . . just fierce

Be fierce – I liked the notion of these queens being fierce.
I put the card in my pocket and bumped slowly forward.

All the wildlife was out. The baby brigade with their pink
plastic tank-tops, Pebbles of the Flintstones haircuts,
yellow-painted faces, oversized red-lipsticked ghoulish
mouths, standing in platform sneakers, shorts, and thigh-
high striped socks, smoking, drinking and talking with the
Sister and Bella and Chucky and all the other fabulous
queens. The body-builders swaggered through the com-
press, their shirts off, leering at anything that looked female.

One of the investors in the club stood at the crowded
bar. As I passed, I heard him shout, 'Tell her who I am!
Tell her I own this fucking place!' This investor owned
about the floorspace of the girl he was trying to pick up.
He was always asking the barstaff to tell whatever girl he
was hitting on how important he was. It was the same
every Saturday night. Everybody on the make for something. The girls were buying the boys drinks, and even
those thrifty sorts that had come to the bar earlier in the
night just after the doors had opened, politely enquiring

150

about the price of a drink, had thrown money cares out the window and were now happy with their cocktail.

I went down the back stairs and passed an hour at Sabina's bar. I shoved cups in ice, filled them with mixed drinks, took the money, made change, over and over, non-stop.

Someone started something. Vaughn and Wayne pulled someone off the floor with a bloody face. Eyelids were down to half mast. $10 bags of coke were going quick in the men's room. The club kids, the ones shaved bald but for four maroon pig-tails placed around the skull, danced together in a group in front of the bar. A go-go box was vacated. One climbed up on to it, had his drink passed to him, and began to dance in his platform sneakers holding his drink and smoking. Kids high on Ecstasy charged the bar again and again, bouncing up and down to the beat, gleaming and wet with perspiration as they took fistfuls of bev naps to wipe the sweat and whine: 'You don't have a can of soda? Why? Okay, okay – how about *bottled water*? Huh? Please, please tell me you got bottled water! Ya don't?' forgetting this was the fourth or the fifth time they had asked me. And all of this was being nourished by the music of DJ Johnny Casanova. Bring the mood up, down, all it needed was the right record.

Casanova stopped the music. Condensation dripped off the iron roof onto the low-lit bar. Dialogue was sampled from the movie *Scarface*.

'*Is this wha' life is all about?*' the voice asked, washing across the overheated bodies, the jungle eyes, the faces squashed together for the first kiss.

A Hispanic kid with a goatee beard and Stussy cap danced back and forth in front, saying, 'Park it in the rear! Park it in the rear! Park it in the rear!'

Pacino said, 'You have tits, you need a bra – they have little hairs on them. You have a bag for a belly. I have a

151

fucking *jonkee* for a wife. She is so po-lluted she can't haff babies. Is this what life is all about? A jonkee for a wife. A jonkee for a wife . . .'

Police sirens. Casanova sampled, 'Two, three, *break*.' And the music broke. And the house roared. Somebody wanted a drink. Everybody wanted drink. I made lots of drinks.

Amanda, a pretty transsexual, was caught in the flash from an admiring photographer, on her stage on one of four go-go boxes. She smiled. An eighteen-year-old boy stood too stoned to move staring up at her large breasts and full lips as she danced.

A shiny mulatto came up to my bar and grinned. I glimpsed a flash of gold on the teeth. A fist was offered.

'Wassup?'

'Not much,' I said.

This was a young man whose name I never learnt, but he was a highly successful businessman. He had a gold-plated beeper. Instead of one gold chain around his neck, he had about ten. He had gold T-bars on his fingers, a blue Polo button-down shirt, a brown Joseph duffle coat, Comme Des Garcon pants, but he still kept his Clyde Frazers and his Kangol in case anyone should forget where he came from. Above his top lip he had a pencil moustache. His features were broad and African. But he was light-skinned. When he walked he had the deepest dip and the widest roll of any man in the club. Over the months I gave him quick service and he dropped large tips. Kahlua and a splash of milk was the man's preference. We never discussed his business.

Tonight, he said, he was impressed. There was some nice-looking bitches in the house. Better than it had been in here for months.

He wasn't talking about James St James or the Xtrava-ganzas, or any of the crowd that had begun to dance

152

nearby, so I asked him who in particular and he pointed at Amanda. I informed him that Amanda was a lovely lady etc; but she was a man.

'If that ain't a fact,' he said. 'She looking good.'

He then said, because I was sweating, cursing and about to smack this prick who was giving me the runaround, 'Life too much for you, bro? You're lucky I'm here, man. I'm gonna give you a time. Meet me outside, four o'clock.' He danced away into the crowd leaving me a twenty for a seven dollar drink.

A man passed wearing a T-shirt that read QUEER BOY. Another: MARY. Another: QUEEN OF THE RODEO. Gary, a sixteen-year-old grass dealer from Long Island with Medusa's hair and a fourteen-year-old's skin condition, arrived at the bar. He smoked a wood grass pipe. When he shook my hand his fingers crawled up my arm like a large spider: acid shake, he said. That was the last thing he told me that made any sense. He fell to his knees and crawled away, barking.

A Chinese girl in a bikini bottom, high heels, a red see-through hooded top and a tiger tattoo on one shoulder kept walking back and forwards in front of the bar taking her top off and on, then stopping to rub herself from time to time. A kid with a flashlight stood shining the light on her. A couple dry-humped on a go-go box. Not long now, I thought.

'Ladies and gentlemen,' a voice shouted. The house lights were on. The music had finished. 'Boys'n'girls, those who had the operation and those that ain't. Ya don't have to go home – but y'all got to get the fuck out! We're closed!' Bouncer Stevie had spoken. Work for the night had ceased. It was time.

On the street as I came out it was early morning, but it was hot and heavy with humidity. Soon it would be light.

Jeeps, Pathfinders, Troopers and Samurais were arranged double- and triple-parked outside the club. The stereo was very loud, but I was deaf anyway. Yellow cabs crawled past hunting a fare. I heard a squeal of tyres, turned and saw a black Nissan Pathfinder 4-Wheel pull up to the kerb, just in front of where I stood. A door opened.

'Yo, here.'

It was my friend, the businessman. I thought, here is a man who knows how to operate in this other world. He has adapted and thrived. Living at nights suits him. By comparison, I am still in the swamps. I could learn something here. I went over and climbed aboard.

It was cool and air-conditioned inside his truck. I shut the door. Without a word we sped off down the rutted, empty street. There was a telephone, with fluorescent numbers, by the shifter. Dice hung from the overhead. He had some music on: techno.

'Now De Luxe, give the man some medication,' said my friend wiping his nose with his forefinger. 'We'll put it on his tab for the night. We gotta get him prepared. My man, I hope you did good tonight?'

'Can't.'

The comment slipped past along with the buildings and the parked cars. Long slender hands with red polished nails snaked over my shoulder. The hand was green, shaded by the diode car clock. It cradled a small spoon and a dark glass vial. In the rear-view I glimpsed a beautiful black woman with a perm and a perfect smile. But I knew her. She was a man.

'Angel,' she said, 'tell him to take.'

We made a right onto Broadway running a red traffic signal, and headed with purpose and high speed for the Village, where the light was coming up in a dark purple fan behind the buildings. At Union Square, the bums lay

154

asleep on the park benches. A carting truck stopped to collect refuse.

'Now is prime time,' said Angel. 'The networks are ready. Gotta make some connections, you know?'

'Make some connections?'

'That's it. I'm strictly business.'

'Sugar's fierce. Sugar has the power,' said De Luxe.

I heard a sniff, and turning, I saw De Luxe wipe his nose and smile. His eyes watered. 'My nose feels like shit,' he told me.

We went down to Houston. The day was coming up over the rooftops on the East River. We went to the projects, I don't know exactly where. Angel parked on an empty street by an open lot with a wire fence. On a stoop opposite, in the half-light, I saw men at a table with a bottle of Thunderbird, playing dominoes. Somewhere someone was playing Salsa, beautiful Salsa music.

'Give the man another hit,' said Angel. And afterwards, 'Leave us for a minute, if you wouldn't mind.'

I got out the truck. De Luxe followed, then he got back in. I saw him bend to arrange his head over Angel's groin. He did not bother to close the car door.

I walked off. Ahead, on the street corner, the coloured lights of a bodega went round and round a sign: Deli . . . Deli . . . Deli. I went in and bought a beer. The man put it in a brown paper bag and I gave him a dollar and left.

Angel and De Luxe were waiting for me. Angel was smiling. 'We must hurry,' he said. 'Time is defeatin' us.'

'Some beer, please,' said De Luxe. I handed him the can as we walked up the street. He rinsed his mouth and spat in the gutter. The line outside Save the Robots was not long. Angel knew everyone. We passed into the darkness without paying.

'I must do some business,' Angel said, once we had been

155

frisked. 'Make y'self amused. Go with your fellow men – but be ready to roll, brother. I won't be long.'

'Follow me,' said De Luxe.

We went through two low-lit rooms covered in sawdust, passing faceless figures moving in silence. Down in the basement a song was playing: *3 a.m Eternal*. When the men's room was free, we went inside and closed the door. On the wall above the sink was scribbled some graffiti. *Beware the monkey on your back*! it said. A line was drawn through the word *beware* and above someone had written: *Enjoy*.

'Take!' said De Luxe handing me the same small glass vial. De Luxe took a toothbrush and toothpaste from his bag and began very methodically to clean his perfect teeth.

'They was a present from Angel,' said De Luxe. 'You like?' He bared his gums. I nodded. When he had finished he said, 'I do believe, I feel like a new man.' Then he adjusted his skirt. 'Ready, baby?'

We went back outside. I bought us drinks. Angel came up to us, dipping and rolling in his fashion.

'They are happy,' he said. 'We did not miss the connection. I have given.'

'Drink?' I asked.

'We must hurry,' he said, so we went.

We went to places I had never been before: nondescript doors against blank graffitied walls; trap doors in the floors of kitchens in small restaurants where down in the cellar Angel was known and loved. Men in suits sat at tables cleaning pistols, sixty-year-old women sat in front of small mounds of cocaine. Some wept when he entered, to them he was a saint. Mumblings, that's all I heard in these places. An old whore told me how the business had changed. We drank heavily. The more we consumed the more invigorated and happy Angel became.

156

'So mature for a fifteen-year-old – don't you think?' De Luxe whispered in my ear, full of pride.

'Last stop,' Angel said as we climbed back into his car. 'How do you feel, bartender?'

'Not so good.'

'De Luxe, fix him up some more. And yo, your tab is one-hundred-and-forty dollars, my man. Gonna take care of it now or later?'

'Later.'

It was, according to the neon clock on the dash, nine-thirty. Cars were moving around on the streets. We passed through them, probably over them and banged a few too I'd guess. It was hard to tell. Families and shoppers had come into the city from the boroughs for a day of pleasure. The station-wagons were full of kids. The radio said it would reach over a hundred today. Record temperatures. But Angel was content. Business had never been better, he said. Nightclubs – they were his home. His beeper had sounded twice during our tour. Customers had been called, deliveries around lower Manhattan had been made and we had only one more stop.

Another free entrance. A bouncer shooed away a cab that wanted to pick up a fare. Angel danced down the darkened aisle. Aggressive-looking men in leather caps and leather shorts, studded armbands and military boots came towards us in the dim night-light, holding hands. I stumbled against one. 'Be careful,' a big queen hissed.

A trip to the men's room, a dip in the vial, a trip to the bar and somewhere along the way I was separated from Angel and De Luxe. But I met a pretty girl I knew, Ixie. She was very drunk and unhappy. Her friend was off in another part of the club sucking face with some guy. As I sat with her for a while, she stopped every man who passed. 'Mira! Mira!' she shrieked. 'Have you seen my friend?' But

157

no one had. She went off to find the friend. I went to find Angel.

They were in the men's room. We went to a booth. A bouncer came in to stop us but when he saw who it was he said, 'Angel, nice to see you, man.' Angel gave him something.

In the corridor afterwards I met another girl I knew. She told me she was moving to Chicago, she could not cope with the City. She was going home now, to her family – what was I doing?

'I don't know.'

In a small room Bella, the drag queen and Rob, a bartender from work, stood talking with people I didn't recognize. There was a shooting at Red Zone, another at Nell's. Kids between the ages of sixteen and nineteen, both killed. Pascal the bouncer had been slashed and lost an eye. One of the promoter girls who lived with a coke dealer had just tried to commit suicide the night before. I wandered around the club for another couple of hours.

At midday I paid Angel. He was off to church now. I had about four dollars left after a night's work. I started walking, keeping to the shade of the buildings heading south – I think that's where I was going, south, towards the sun, towards Guatemala if I had the opportunity. South where life was a little less bullying. But soon I was too tired and I had to sit down. There was a ragged figure up ahead. A man was squatting in a trickle of urine, eyes closed, smoking from a burnt glass pipe. He paid me no notice. I sat near him and closed my eyes. I could just smell the river when the breeze stirred the still air. Soon I slipped off. A month later I had pneumonia.

Seven

I went home to family. I slept eighteen hours a day, couldn't climb the stairs to my room without wanting to sit down and fall fast asleep, and thought I must have caught AIDS or TB, since I was just a frail skeleton, unable to put a pound on my bony frame. But a local physician ran tests on this body and diagnosed my sickness as a viral pneumonia, with a patch on one lung, the left. He said I'd be back on my feet in two weeks. I was dormant three months.

But whilst enthroned, feverish and fussed over, I had a timely opportunity to brood over my great stake in this world. No matter how I dressed it, it didn't look too pretty. No regular job, no bank account, no savings, no health insurance, no girlfriend, no possessions, no money, zero interests but for books, music and movie-houses. And I had told anyone who cared to listen over the years that I would be a rich man by the time I was forty. When I was finally able to flee the leafy suburbs and white weatherboard prisons, and board the Metro-North Liner for New York City, with a loan from dear Mother, I had come to the inescapable conclusion that I ought to experiment with something radical and never contemplated in the past. A career. This was what I concluded must be missing from my glamorous life. Prospects. Security for the future. Carla, my old snookums, had a future.

She had called me at the house when I was sick. She

said she had never been happier. She now had a house and two kids and a job at a sports clothing store in town. She went to the supermarket on Saturdays and they went to the beach on Sundays. Her husband was going to buy a bass boat soon and she hoped that they'd be able to afford a house on the lake to allow him to spend his weekend fishing. Carla's stake in the world had gone up. And she had plans for the future. She was talking about setting up a small catalogue clothing business. She said she wasn't one to nag or anything, but there comes a time you've got to grow up and join the real world. Quite.

My real world was a bum job, a fuck-up if I got lucky and a mattress that poked me in the left ear when I slept at night. It was a can of beer on the way home from work. It was always being late with the rent and never having enough to cover the bills when they came in. It was rarely being able to go out. It was being cruelly denied, as I discovered when I got back to the city, the chance to go to the wedding of a good friend on the west coast. No lolly. That was my real world, as Carla would say. And I didn't like it anymore. I had had a nice time skipping about and trying my hand at different things but now I wanted full money mobility. An all-terrain, four-wheel drive, fully loaded career.

Glorious. A pay-cheque that didn't bounce. A bank account. A credit card. Able to look the Mr Ed Philistine in the eye when he darkened our doors threatening to throw off the electricity, and write him a cheque. Eat lunch in a restaurant when I was hungry. Take pussy to the vet. Have health insurance. Wake the landlord in the middle of the night to thrust the rent in his fat paw. These were the sorts of things I had begun to entertain as fantasies. Not too unreasonable, you know.

My only problem was this: I was not eligible to do anything you got paid well to do. Media, sports, industry, news – no good for me. A college education was needed. Entrepreneurial activity was a possibility, but since the hot dogs I hadn't been struck by any great dynasty-building ideas.

The days passed. Unfortunately, I began to slip into darkness. After a couple of weeks of enthusiastic but unsuccessful sorties in the 'wanted' columns, I formed the distinct impression that I would become one of the exiled, a bum with a hole in the seat of his pants, snoozing on a park bench in Union Square, panhandling for money in the not too distant future. I would be the man opening the door for you at Citibank, the man with an empty coffee-cup, saying 'Spare a dime please, if you can.' I was becoming resigned to this as I checked the papers for work. And I imagine I would have stayed that way, too, if it weren't for one day when a great uplifting experience occurred.

I was down in Brownies at the time, sipping the last pint of fine Guinness stout I could afford, when in came this expensively-dressed man.

This man swagged up to the bar, full of confidence, ordered himself a drink, and turned to me and said, holding out his hand, 'Bob. Account Executive: WWB & D. How ya doin'?'

I told him I was doing and he seemed pleased by this. We shook hands. The barman poured his drink, and as Bob sat himself on the stool next to mine, I thought: this fish is in the wrong pond. No man in Brownies wears linen and loafers.

Bob told me he was in the advertising business. 'I handle a lotta important accounts. You know what I mean?'

'Not really.'

'Ever heard of SuperChow?'

'No.'

'SuperChow is my account. It's a special dog food where

the dogs don't have to do doo-doo. You know what I mean? It's going to revolutionize the pet business.'

'That's very interesting, Bob,' I said.

'Yeah,' he replied. He leant behind me to look out through the glass. 'Say, is a nice car safe round here?'

'I wouldn't know,' I said. 'From what?'

'Theft. My car alarm ain't working.'

I shrugged. No neighbourhood is safe and having never owned a car I wouldn't know anyway. Bob loosened his floral kipper tie. He told me the reason he was so concerned about the neighbourhood was because he had just bought himself a new automobile.

'A five-series Beemer,' he said, 'loaded. I park it in the underground parking facility of my condo I just moved to over in Battery Park City. Nice spot. You know what I mean?'

I smiled. Old Bob was pitching me his life. He didn't need my opinions or conversation.

'Tell you what, Bob,' I said. 'Why don't you buy me a little drink?'

He did. Over the next ten minutes I learnt more things about Bob than I knew about most people. I learnt how many times Bob went to the movies each week (three, action pictures were his favourite), how often he went out to dinner (six or seven – uptown, downtown, anywhere she wanted to go), how many cocktail parties he went to (three or four), how much his rent was (twenty-four-hundred a month), how many girls he was seeing (three – one was English, but he hadn't slept with her yet), how many Armani suits he owned (four), how much his summer share in the house in East Hampton cost (nine-hundred a month), his thoughts on politics ('fucking democrats – nuke the bastards!') and America ('the greatest country in the world!'); and finally himself ('just a regular guy, out to make a shit-load of money. You know what I mean?').

162

Through all this crap I listened and was rewarded with a number of drinks. This was the only reason I stayed in the place. As I sucked down the beers Bob pitched me more bull, but returned, time after time, to the one thing he felt truly defined him: his career, advertising.

'It's really, really me,' he told me for the fourth time. 'You know what I mean?'

'I'll take a pint.'

Bob then grabbed my wrist. 'But you know what really gets up my fucking arse? Huh?'

'No,' I said.

'Copywriters! Assholes come in without fucking degrees, write one crummy campaign and the little fucking jerkoffs are treated like they just won the Superbowl or something. You know what I mean? Makes me puke.'

'Without a degree?'

'No fucking education. And I spent *six years* in school. I got an education. Business Studies at the University of Boston. I went in at entry level and worked my tail off until I was like, you know, an account executive. With my own client list. Then some little prick who ain't even old enough to have butt-hair enters the agency and within six months he's at the same salary I'm making and telling *me* what the fuck to do! Makes me heave, man. You know what I mean?'

'Without a degree?'

'Without a degree. Now where's the justice? Huh? Any moron can write advertising. Even you.'

This was the first thing that Bob had said that I wanted to hear. Someone who got paid a lot of money for a job, who had absolutely no qualifications. Far away, I began to hear the angels tipping off their bar stools.

'And how much money is made, exactly, by these pricks?' I asked Bob.

'The good ones? Two, two-hundred-and-fifty-thou a year easy.'

'For writing slogans?'

'Yeah, that piece a shit. It's a fucking joke.'

Joke or not, I reckon at that very moment the celestial hordes descended noisily into the bar at Brownies dancing an eight-reel jig, with cherubs on the fiddles. And to help me recognize the presence of this great opportunity, sunbeams split the clouds and light streamed through the windows and made gleaming pools and columns of splendid bright light on the bar floor. At least, this is how I liked to remember it. My four-pint epiphany.

I smiled. Advertising. This was how a man like me could own a bank account. I looked at this Bob with the tanned face and sixty-dollar haircut, the three-hundred-dollar alligator loafers with tassles and toe cleavage and pink socks; the baggy and crumpled linen suit, the loud tie, the physique of a health-nut and I thought to myself: that's what I want to be. Like him. I want the fat trimmings of the good life. I want a fully-loaded BMW and expense account. I want a condo in Battery Park City overlooking the harbour lights of Manhattan Bay. I want some ugly alligator-skin loafers from Cole-Haan that'll cost me a month's rent. I do. Gimme. Even if I buy the shoes just to sling 'em out the window at anything riding a Harley.

From that moment forth I became an enlightened man, a disciple of Bob's, greedy for knowledge about his great business and super wonderful magazine life. What a beautiful life it was, though. Weekends down to the Bahamas with some lady ('a model or an actress, can't be older than twenty-five, a dazzling dresser, no cellulite, no morals, and a whore in bed – that's the way I like 'em,' said Bob). Or off to blast doves in the Carolinas staying on some plantation somewhere. And during the week he ate at the best restaurants in town, places I'd walked past many times over the years but had never been inside. He went to the movies when he wanted, and the theatre, and the opera, too, with a different girl every night. Bob had freedom. Bob had a career. And he had stumbled into a little bar like Brownies totally by chance. I made sure Bob and myself became great pals.

I told Bob blonde jokes. Bob loved blonde jokes. I told Bob labourer jokes. I schmoozed him with sporting news. And later, as we weaved uptown careful of pot holes, cabs and other cars in the deluxe, leather-upholstered BMW, listening through thumping speakers to a lame pop song, I thought to myself: this is the life for a man of 29th Street.

I had Bob's card – embossed, impressive, beautiful; a promise to introduce me to the person responsible for hiring at a prestigious Madison Avenue advertising agency; and a list of books to read and study if I was truly interested in becoming a big-earning, mass-copulating, copywriter, Godhead, advertising super-stud and frequent flyer.

I bounded home that night in robust form. Life, for the first time in months, was rosy. And all it took was a bit of hope.

Over the next couple of months, I got busy. I spent the day working a mutt's job, but at night I sat with pots of steaming Medaglio d'Oro coffee at Pedro's rickety art-board desk, below a cluster of plastic grapes in the front room, and composed great advertisements.

Writing advertising was easy. All I had to do was write about things I wanted: credit cards, bars, holidays, sail-boats, trucks, slot-car tracks. I had a fine time imagining product benefit. And it was like going off to work in a pleasure park for the evening: great rides constructed from the prose of product benefit and the testimonial. Within five weeks I was ready and I called Bob.

Bob didn't remember me. When I reminded him who I was, of that great night we'd had drinking Guinness, of my boozy epiphany, my new-found Americanness, my desire for a glorious career in the advertising business, he was slow to acknowledge all the fine things and great promises of introductions and help he had offered me the night we got stinky together. I think he had forgotten. Eventually he said, 'Ah, now it's coming back to me. Your name is Jimmy, right?'

No, but I had made contact with the extra-terrestrial. That was the important thing. Besides, I had to take into consideration that this was a man who had a lot on his mind: deals, lunches at Le Cirque, secretaries, pitches, shoots, English girls, dove-slaughtering, and a wild social schedule. It was only natural that his memory needed a little jolt. So once contact had been established I immersed him in conversation about the one thing that interested Bob most in life: himself. I asked him about the surly concierge at his building, the big accounts he must have landed. Those weekends in the Bahamas with that English uptown babe, the processed blonde, the one that called him 'Sir' when he did her – what was her name?

'Lucinda.'

'That's it, Lucinda. How is she doing?'

'Fell to pieces,' said Bob. 'And that was after I spent a fucking fortune on her. You know where we went? Au Bar. Ever been there? Place is full of rich fucking pricks. I love it. But what happened? She met some Viscount the same night and ran off with him. And *I* bought the champagne. All night. For the three of us. God knows what it must've cost me. She's back in England now. Look pal, things are kinda tricky around here at the moment. I don't know if you've been reading about it but business is going through some tough times. Even Saatchis is deep in the fucking shit. We're in a recession.'

'Bob,' I said. 'Listen, I've been in a recession for the last ten years now. Maybe longer. I want to see you. I have

166

great work to show you. Stuff that might make a difference to your . . .'

But Bob wasn't interested. I tried some new blonde jokes. This got me back into the conversation. He said, maybe we should meet sometime, then he could look at my work and give an opinion as to what to present and what not to; but he couldn't guarantee anything.

'Fine,' I said. 'I'll see you tonight, five-thirty.'

'Hold your horses, pal. I can't do tonight. I gotta make a pitch this afternoon. It's going to go late.'

'All right. How about tomorrow? Would tomorrow be better for you, Bob? Would tomorrow . . .'

'Whoa, man! Whoa!'

'Bob, I need an interview. Please. Please . . .'

Bob agreed to help which was all I was asking for, a little helping hand to look at the work, make a couple of calls, open a few doors – for as Bob said, 'It's not what you know but *who* you know. Contacts are the lifeblood of a successful career. Nothing more than that.' And that's all I was after. A career. It would be a great success just to get one.

A week later I met Bob in a sports bar on the Upper West Side and showed him my book.

'These are luxury products,' Bob told me. 'You can't put a book together full of luxury products. And fucking slot-car tracks, man – how the fuck can you expect to bill off that?'

I shrugged.

'Luxury products are prestige accounts. They don't make the agency rich. Here's what you gotta do . . .'

Go off and write a bunch of ads about crummy soap powders, toothpaste, and other difficult-to-get-excited-about products. But writing this stuff got on my tits. It was no fun. Within three weeks I was ready with new work and some of it Bob approved of. Two weeks after that Bob said

I was ready and hooked me up with an appointment to see a major advertising firm on Madison Avenue, McCann & Erikson.

The first proper interview of my shabby life. I was a little lost as to what was needed to be appropriately dressed. I felt I ought to try to look like Bob but I had no money to clobber Emporio Armani, Paul Smith, or Cole-Haan. So I borrowed thirty bucks from the newsman and went to the thrift store with Ramin, the dandy Persian. Ram took me to the best Thrift stores in the city and by the end of two days of walking the streets I had been outfitted in glorious 1970s discarded clothing. I bought a second-hand suit a little short in the arms and legs but definitely with the requisite baggy-linen-just-slept-in look about it – probably because I plucked it from one of the bins. I bought some aerodynamic patent leather shoes for five dollars and change. I bought a big kipper tie with a picture of Carmen Miranda dancing with a bowl of fruit on her head. I borrowed some of the newsman's socks and tucked the holes down the sides of the loafer. Then, when I was all assembled and was standing facing the mirror on the morning of my big day I realized something was definitely missing. Somewhere I had read that red suspenders were the very fashion for men on the fast track. The newsman had a set, I remembered. I looted his closet and found some on the floor behind the laundry bag. After dusting them off, I put them on and measured my appearance.

I looked terrible, no getting away from it. But as long as I didn't look disrespectful, as long as I tried to fit in, that was what was called for, I hoped.

9:30 on the morning of this great event, I woke the newsman who was still snoring under the covers in his bed. (He had a cushy job with the cable news channel that did not require his presence much before 10:30. Over the years,

I always woke him around this time to tell him his bath was running.)

'Wish me luck,' I said when I'd shaken him.

'Where are you going?'

'Job interview.'

'Buy some milk when you come back.'

That was all he had to say about the day that was going to change my life.

The building up on Lexington Avenue wasn't magnificent or impressive but I could walk to it from the loft, so it was beautiful, in my eyes.

Inside, the security gave me a pass and sent me to the back of the building to catch a ride up to the thirty-sixth floor. At the elevator bank I stood in line with my fellow working professionals, nodding and smiling to them all. It felt deeply satisfying not to be taking the freight elevator.

I got out at McCann's floor to face a bronze bust of the founding father of this great institution – Mr McCann or Mr Erikson, I'm not sure which. But underneath the noble head were written the words: *The Truth Well Told*. What, I puzzled, had that got to do with advertising?

I moved on to the receptionist's desk and mentioned the name of the lady I had come to see. I was told to sit for a moment. The decor in the place was conservative. Some might say drab, but as I was here for a job, I preferred conservative. It was grey. It had what looked like carpet stapled to the walls. In fact, it was just a notch up in decor from a government building. But at least there were no carpet tiles. I sat in a big, comfy chair and fidgeted.

Not so long after, a middle-aged lady appeared, very prim and smart, and told me some news. The lady I had come to see, who normally did the book-seeing and who was a 'personal' friend of Bob's (most important), could not see me, but a top copy-writer, a man keen to keep tabs

169

on the new talent that came through the doors in the agency, could.

'But does he know Bob?' I asked.

'Who?'

This was a bad start. I was led down a long corridor to a small office and left on my own. As I stood and waited I realized the suit I was wearing stank of mothballs.

A couple of minutes passed. No-one showed. The office was small, more like the pictures I had seen in the magazines of advertising agencies. It was organized, modern and full of things that were matt black: the table, the phone, a cup with matt black pens, a desk organizer, a leather filofax, a calculator with huge numbers on it, and other vital tools. This was more like what I had expected – uptight and Italian, not City Hall with a facelift. The shelves behind the swivel chair were also matt black. Big, weighty volumes of the *Advertising Art Director's Guild Award* books line them: the years 1961 to the present day.

As I was looking at these books the door opened behind me. A short, stocky man marched straight past me to the desk and then sat at it. He had short-cropped grey hair, an emerald green Lacoste shirt, khaki chinos and white Stan Smith tennis shoes. Copy-writer fashion, I thought. More relaxed and loose. No need to make any statement here other than that we're the top dogs, not the suits. I kicked myself for not having been smart enough to make the distinction. Bob was a suit. Suits do business at lunch. Copy-writers play table tennis or pool at lunch. Ties get in the way of that.

The man finally looked up at me. Then for a long time he gazed at me, sort of puzzled.

'What's your name?' he asked.

I told him.

'Show me your book.'

I passed it to him. It was in black plastic that had cost

170

me six dollars and change from Sam Flax Stationers, Park Avenue.

He flicked through the pages and I waited to see some telling sign that he was deeply impressed. No chance.

'Quite frankly,' he said, looking up after a too quick flick through months of my labour, 'I think some of this is the most offensive advertising I have ever seen.'

'Oh.'

This man made his crust as a master of the bullshit. And what did I know? My expertise in the field of advertising was limited to handing out flyers for Stouffers New! Chicken Dinner at Sloan's Supermarket on the Upper East Side. People paid him money, good money. He had to know what he was talking about. But instead of making a swift kill of me and despatching me with a cruel flick of the wrist and an admonishment for wasting his precious creative time, the man turned to two advertisements, right at the end of my book, that I had written for Visa credit cards. The ads took the form of letters written by a man called Herman to his friend Barney back home at The Hunt and Fish Club in Holyoke, Mass. Herman was retired, now off on permanent vacation with his wife, Mildred, a devout Catholic, a player of the rosary beads, a blue-rinse devil in orthopaedic shoes. The letters told of Herman's adventures whilst trying to give the old bat the slip so he could skip into the bar for a pop. But, as the woman always kept his wallet, the only way the man could ever indulge was on his wonderful, totally consumer-friendly credit card that was accepted everywhere he went, any time he went there, without fail. These letters took the form of a comic adventure. The man liked them.

'But,' he said, 'they'd never work. You can't have him leaving his wife to go off and get drunk. That's not acceptable to a sponsor. Besides, they're too print-heavy.'

Too print-heavy. But something had happened. I had made a connection.

'So, tell me please – what do you think good advertising is?' I asked, eager and keen and ready to pounce again on opportunity.

The man reached behind and pulled from the shelf one of the volumes of award books. He laid it out in front of me. 'Come here,' he said.

I craned my neck over the desk to see. I did not want to put him off by my rank smell. The senior copy-writer flicked through the glossy pages and then stopped at a page and ran his finger up the gutter of the book.

'This,' the man said suddenly pointing down at a glossy page, 'is great advertising.'

I looked down. The advertisement was for Harley-Davidson motor-cycles. The picture showed a gang of dirty child molesters and hog-fuckers who rode bikes. Above them in thick black box print was a headline: *Would You Sell A Bad Motor-Cycle To These Guys?*

'No,' I said.

'Great advertising. You believe it.'

'The truth well told,' I said, trying to score a few points.

'Exactly.'

He picked up my book again and flicked through it.

'Your problem is you try to entertain. America is a land of shop-keepers and merchants. We like to be sold to. We want to know *why* something is good. We want to know the truth about it. Advertising is a great force. It changes lives. It's very powerful. You just gotta know how to sell. Do you understand?'

He smiled, folded my book shut, and pushed it across his desk.

'So what do you suggest I do?' I asked.

'Well, we do have an opening here for a junior copy-writer . . .'

And as those words fell off his tongue and filled my ears, my eyes lit up and as my guts were a little rotten with coffee, I let fly a silent fart. I moved further away from his desk and smiled.

He picked up a paperclip from one of the matt black cups. He presented it.

'Write me a campaign about this over the weekend and I'll see what I can do,' he told me.

I bolted from that office – never have I thanked someone so much. In my hand I clutched my houses, wives, kiddies, toys, dogs, cats, all dependent on this paperclip. My diamond. My gilt-edged long-term investment bond.

I hit Lexington Avenue at full throttle. Not a minute to waste. Seventy-two hours to come up with something original, ground-breaking, great and never before said or thought about the wonderful paperclip. When I came to a Sam Flax I ducked inside and ran up to the counter.

'Well,' I said to the man holding aloft my clip. 'What about it? Who makes this paperclip, please?'

The manager smiled. 'Noestings,' he said after closer inspection.

'No what?'

'Noestings. Here, lemme write it down for you. Look. There.'

'Do they make anything else?'

'I don't know. You'll have to ring them up. They're over in the Bronx.'

I thanked him, snatched the clip from his claw, put it in my pocket and ran back through the lunchtime crowd on 5th but discovered I had no keys and worse, no great ideas. I was a blank. No one was at home being near twelve so I had to ring the landlord's bell. The upstairs door to the home was always open because it had never been locked and there was nothing much worth stealing.

I explained my problem, I was let in, but I got cornered
173

as I tried to run past the studio door. Some questions, the fat man said, rubbing his hands together and then settling to excavate his right nostril with the pinkie on his left hand.

'Can't,' I said. 'Haven't time.'

'Why?'

'Because . . . because of this!' But when I pulled out my trouser pocket lining I found a big hole in my second-hand suit. The clip had fallen through. I bolted for the stairs.

Up at the loft I started to panic. The space was a bombsite. Normal, in other words. Not a place I could work in.

The truth well told, I muttered . . . The truth – but I had no ideas.

I ran to the sink. A pile of cracked plates and burnt pans spilled over onto the draining board. I burrowed a hand down and freed the swill-hole of chilli beans.

You can't be successful if you live like this, I thought. Must be orderly. Like those desks. Like those offices. Like those offices where I might be employed if I could think of . . . *Noestings paperclips hold papers together. Noestings paperclips hold all papers together. The indestructible Noestings paperclip is not like any other paperclip because* – no, no, no.

Seventy-one hours, seventeen minutes and, oof, help.

I filled the sink with warm water. The leaky collar on the tap sprouted a geyser of water at the back wall. Be tidy, I thought. To work . . . *A thousand uses for Noestings paperclips: You can clip 'em* . . . The truth. The truth was I couldn't think of a thing.

Plates were washed. Counters got a wipe. A bowl of fresh water was put down for the cat. I changed. Time: Seventy hours, fifty-eight minutes and forty-three, forty-two, forty-one . . .

What to say?

I went to the table, pulled out the armless armchair, arranged my pad, arranged my pen, got up, fetched a specimen jar from the cabinet above the sink, filled it with water, laid it one inch from the border of the pad, corrected its position, then when I was at a loss as to what else to do the phone went.

Over the speakerphone for the answer-machine I heard a creditor from the Citibank seeking restitution from the newsman, leaving a number he could call anytime, day or night. Ninety-per-cent of all voice mail on the machine was from creditors. And I had a paperclip and . . . *Noestings! America's number one* . . . no, no, no.

Seventy hours and forty minutes. Seventy hours and thirty-nine minutes and . . .

After fifteen minutes of staring at the empty page and gouging the last stubs of nails from my fingers I picked up the phone and dialled information. A few calls later I was talking to the office manager of the Noestings main office in the Bronx. I explained my troubles. What could the good man tell me about this fabulous paperclip?

'Well, it's made of metal so it doesn't break.'

Doesn't break, I wrote on my paper underlining it five times.

'What else?'

'It's magnetized.'

Magnetized, I wrote, but this was not giving me point of sales purchase. Nothing to distinguish this clip from a million other clips.

'Is it cheaper than other clips?' I asked.

'No,' he said. 'About the same.'

About the same, I wrote.

'Are you the only manufacturer of magnetized paper-clips?'

'Nope.'

'I see. Well do you make any other types of paperclips? You know, plastic, coloured or . . .?'

'No.'

175

'A-ha. Well, do you make anything else at all, besides paperclips – race cars, jet fighters or . . .?'

'No.'

I was just ready to put the phone down when the man said something that got the bells ringing. 'Well, of course, we are the sole supplier of paperclips to the library of the House of Congress, and have been for the last fifty years,' he said.

That was it, I thought. The library of the House of Congress. The keeper of the nation's culture. It wouldn't do to have a rusty clip on that, now would it? What if the Constitution got a nasty big rust mark all over it? Or the Bill of Rights? Bye-bye freedom of speech. What a time I could have with rust and a general re-organization of those pesky laws that got in the way of the individual's right to enjoy himself. But is that reason enough for a person to buy a paperclip? Anyway, who cares if the library of the House of Congress chooses this paperclip? Maybe they got a special deal, I asked.

The man said, 'No. They choose our clips because they don't break, don't rust and are magnetized. All right?'

'I see. Thank you very much.'

But I didn't really see. I put the phone down. Hours passed. The paper was filled with doodles. But I had no great ideas. Nothing that sold the clip rather than amused me. Near six that night the boys came home. Both had an armful of new records from Downtown and Vinyl Mania. Great tunes. And beer. And food. It was Friday night and on Friday nights . . .

'No music!' I shouted.

Slogan writing under pressure isn't easy. Fifty-one-thousand ways of saying nothing but superlatives. The truth well told and all that – but what was so life-changing about a paperclip? I was struggling. It wasn't like a car where you could find a million ways of saying something about going fast, or going slow, or reliability, or economy, or warranty, or its bigger brother being a jet fighter. Nothing was quite as boring as a paperclip and that was why I had been given it. If I could say something interesting about this, anything would be possible. Trouble was, I couldn't.

Why would you buy one clip over another when they cost the same, look the same, and for all intents and purposes are the same? I wondered. Maybe a bit of product identification was needed here. A bikini contest with paperclip bikinis. The Noestings Beach Invitational . . .

I needed help. Suddenly I hated advertising. Days passed slowly and with great agony, but nothing much happened creatively except for the fights I had with the boys. I couldn't eat, couldn't drink, couldn't talk. I was miserable. But on the day of the Sabbath I was touched by the Good Fella. I had a shake. My fist started to draw an ad. A paperclip. Above the paperclip I wrote: *Potentially the most ruinous force to American culture*. Below I wrote the blurb. Then the tag line: *Noestings: We Hold America Together*. That was it. Creation and Deliverance.

But at what cost? Fifty-four hours and forty-seven minutes of getting cross-eyed staring at a paperclip, gallons of coffee, packets of cigarettes, a dark mood, a narrowing of all interests in the past months to thirty-second television commercials and magazine print advertisements; and a brain currently on a continuous dreamloop of a paperclip. Being obsessed with a paperclip disturbed me more than worrying about money. Ad-land had become my universe. I didn't like it.

Maybe, I thought, when the ads were all drawn, I was not built for copy-writing. Maybe the linen suits, tasselled loafers and pink socks weren't for me. Maybe 29th Street and mugs with no handles and plates that were cracked and chairs that were broken and bath that overflowed and

177

doors that were bust and even the landlord coming up in the middle of the night to shout and scream was more my speed.

My epiphany, I decided, wasn't what I had expected it to become. After months of writing advertisements I had come to the conclusion I hated it. And I found that the boys at the loft were tiring of my new fervent desire to have a career. Noise curfews, no late night carousing, a compulsion to switch channels so the television was always tuned for an advertisement. A debt with each member of the household – I had a monumental one-hundred-and-thirty-four dollars to repay. They were fed up, so was I.

On the morning of my second interview, the newsman, standing in his open bathrobe, dripping with bath-water, member hanging out, had a few words to say.

'Your interview today?'

'Yes.'

'For your sake I hope you don't get it.'

At 10 a.m. I was led into the office to present The Work: three roughs, six days in purgatory; me: a skinny-boned jittery mess.

'How old are you?' I was asked.

'Twenty-three,' I lied.

'That's what I told them. Well, let's see it.'

I slipped him three pieces of paper. On each page was an ad. He picked them up one by one and studied them slowly. Then he returned to the first ad and held it up at arm's length. It was the potentially most, blah, blah, blah.

'I like this,' he said. 'But what do you mean?'

I explained the blab. Noestings being the sole supplier to the library of the House of Congress on all-important documents, how important it was that the clip never break, never rust, etc.

The ad seemed to strike a chord with my Bhagwan. And the tag line. He liked that, too. On the subject of holding

178

America together he mentioned that Mr Ronald Reagan had asked him to write the advertising for his campaign for re-election all those years ago.

'Oh? What did you say?'

'No.'

'Why?'

'I told you. Advertising is powerful. It shouldn't be used in the wrong hands. I only write stuff I believe.'

I knew advertising was powerful. I was testament to that fact. It was all I ever dreamt of. I asked him if he thought it was good enough to take upstairs to the big Gods of the agency.

He smiled.

'You will?' I asked.

'Sure, I'll give it a try.'

I left my book with him. Maybe, I thought, it would all get easier when somebody paid me money; but secretly I had a nasty suspicion it wouldn't. It would get worse. If I felt all this just looking for a job, without a client or boss on my back, what was I going to feel when I had a job and people paid me money and expected work? Worse. It could only be worse.

'Ah,' said the newsman as we sat drinking in Joe's that night. 'But at least you'll have money in your pocket.'

Days later, just before I headed out the door and went off to work, the phone rang. For a change, it wasn't a creditor.

'Got some news for you,' the senior copy-writer from McCann and Erikson said.

'When do I start?'

'You don't. Sorry, kid. The boss didn't bite. He wanted someone who could sell better. Your problem, as I told you, is you try to entertain. You know what you should do? You should try writing.'

I was silent.

179

'But I tell you what,' said the man, 'my wife works over at Saatchis. Let me keep your book and I'll give it to her. Maybe they're looking for people.'

Not if Bob was to be believed.

As the weeks of waiting for an answer from the man's wife passed, I slowly disengaged my interests from the advertisements and slipped back into old habits. Loud music. Friday nights with Ramin and Pedro and the newsman and the ladies from bar to party to bar to club. Old ways. People came over to the loft and we drank and smoked and talked until three, four in the morning. I had made an effort and had a look at the career game and it stank. Plates piled up in the sink. Cans of Budweiser returned to the refrigerator. The sofa mattress was not sought until 4 a.m. I sat and read books again. I did not pick up one magazine. I never watched commercials. Everything went back to normal. And I liked it.

Some months after I had given up all hope of a career in advertising, I was down in Brownies again for a pint. I was with the boys from the loft and I had some news. That afternoon I had bumped into Bob on the street, but Bob had lost his linen suit, expensive loafers, and floral kipper tie. He was dressed as if it was a weekend, but it was midday, lunchtime, when we met. He looked haggard, unshaven, his hair was a mess and his jeans dirty.

'Bob,' I had said to him. 'What are you doing here? Why aren't you at work?'

'I don't have any work to go to any more.'

'Why – they fire you?' I joked.

Bob was silent.

'They did? No shit.'

'Fucking Republicans,' said Bob. 'You don't know how bad my life is. I lost my car, my condo – my fucking life.' Bob started to cry.

180

I asked him what he was going to do and he said he didn't know.

'Ever thought of labouring? I tell you what – house-painting is a fine job. I might be able to hook . . .'

'Are you crazy? That's beneath me. I gotta business degree from the University of Boston. Are you crazy?'

I shrugged.

'What happened with your job?' Bob asked me.

'Didn't get it. Must have been nuts to even start thinking about it.'

'So why did ya?'

'Feeling insecure.'

Bob looked at me and shook his head. Then without another word he drifted off into the afternoon crowd.

I told the boys this because we were all drifting apart, too. The newsman was moving to Washington, Pedro was going off to study architecture in London and I had decided to stay at 29th Street if I could. I was going to take the copy-writer's advice.

A week later was Gay Pride Day in New York. Allied Movers had been in the house moving out the newsman. I went out to the store before the beginning of the parade to buy a bacon, lettuce and tomato sandwich and as I stood at the side of the road, eating my sandwich, a young queen in the tightest shorts I had seen in a long time came striding up the street, and stopped right opposite me.

'You're looking nice!' he said.

'I'm feeling nice,' I replied.

'I can see it. Mmh-hmm.'

Then he marched off and started waving to the passing traffic. I went home and that day I set to work.

Not so long ago, Carla and her husband came to town with their kids. He was a great man. After Carla and the kids had gone back to the hotel we spent a night drinking down in the East Village. He asked me what I was doing

181

and I told him I was trying to write this book. He said I ought to go live with them whilst I wrote. Then I wouldn't have to worry about the rent. I thanked him but I knew I was never going to leave. I was happy at 29th Street, with my work, and you couldn't ask for much more than that. So, I thank you boys for those days. What a fine time it all was.

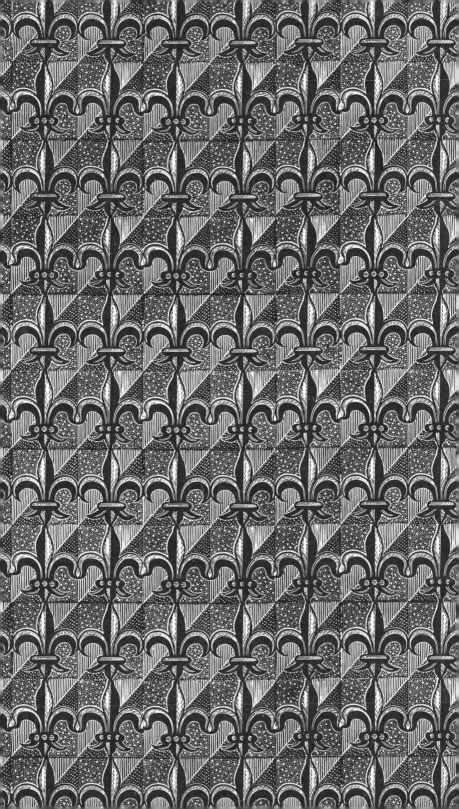